11/59

FIRST INTO OUTER SPACE

# FIRST
# INTO OUTER
# SPACE

*THEODORE J. GORDON*
*and JULIAN SCHEER*

*ILLUSTRATED*

*ST MARTIN'S PRESS · NEW YORK*

TO THE TEAM

# ACKNOWLEDGMENT

The authors gratefully acknowledge the cooperation and assistance of the Department of Defense, Advanced Research Projects Agency, National Aeronautics and Space Administration, the United States Air Force, USAF Ballistic Missile Division, the Douglas Aircraft Co. Inc., The Charlotte *News*, the Air Force Missile Test Center, Patrick AFB, Florida.

# ILLUSTRATIONS

## PHOTO CREDITS

Official United States Air Force Photos Pages 2, 7, 11, 37,
49, 52, 53, 55, 56, 69, 73, 77, 91, 115, 121, 133, 134, 145,
153, 179, 180, 185
Department of Defense Photos Pages 59, 95, 99, 107,
136, 137, 149, 163, 167, 171, 172
North American Aviation Photos Pages          45, 46

# GLOSSARY

## A

ABLE—Code name given to the THOR-boosted, multi-stage vehicles employing modified Vanguard second stages.

ACCELEROMETER—A sensing device carried aboard a missile to detect rate of change of velocity. Sometimes used as a telemetry instrument or in control or guidance systems.

ARM—To activate an explosive or igniting circuit.

ATTITUDE—The position of an object in space as determined by the inclination of its axes to some frame of reference.

AZUSA—A high-accuracy trajectory determining system developed by Convair. Employs phase comparison techniques between several ground antennas to determine the location of a missile in flight.

## B

BALLISTIC MISSILE—A vehicle whose flight path from engine burn-out is "free flight" like that of any projectile; it is subject to gravitation and drag and may or may not perform maneuvers to modify or correct the flight path.

BEACON—A missile-carried radio transmitter, usually of high frequency and relatively low power, that can be followed by ground tracking stations. The term is also used loosely to include transponders that serve much the same purpose but transmit only after receiving an interrogating pulse from the ground station.

BIRD—Slang for missile.

BLOCKHOUSE—The reinforced concrete building that houses the firing crew and equipment during a launching.

BOOSTER—An auxiliary propulsion system that travels with the missile and may or may not separate from the missile when its impulse has been delivered.

## C

CELLS—Short term for Load Cells, devices which detect the weight of the missile and generate an electrical signal proportionate to that weight.

CENTRAL CONTROL—The building at Cape Canaveral that houses Range Command, i.e. the Superintendent of Range Operations, the Range Safety Officer, Interference Control, etc.

CHAMBER PRESSURE—The gas pressure that exists inside the combustion chamber of a burning rocket engine.

CHARTS—Used here as graphical presentations of the variations of a function.

COMMAND RECEIVER—A missile-carried receiver designed to detect the Safety Officer's destruct command. When it receives this command, it activates explosive devices that destroy the missile.

COMPLEX—Short term for launching complex, or that group of facilities required for a missile launching, including among other things the blockhouse, launching pad, and shop building.

CONSOLE—Desk-like operating or monitoring equipment.

COUNTDOWN—An organized series of checks and rechecks conducted while finally preparing a missile for firing or launching.

CRITIQUE—The post-flight meeting during which the first consolidated concept of the test results is formed.

## D

DECLINATION—The angle between earth's equatorial plane and a heavenly body.

DEFLECTOR PLATE—The heavy, steel, water-cooled plate that deflects the rocket exhaust flame harmlessly toward an open area.

DELUGE WATER—The water supply designed to extinguish fires in case of a major catastrophe during launch.

DESTRUCT—To destroy an errant missile that threatens to endanger life or property.

DISPERSION—The deviation of a missile's flight path from that predicted.

## E

ELSSE—Electronic sky screen equipment, a range safety system.

EQUATORIAL PLANE—The projection of the plane of the earth's equator upon the celestial sphere.

ESCAPE VELOCITY—The velocity that if reached by a body will allow it to escape the earth's primary field of gravity.

EXPLORER—The code name applied to the series of earth satellites launched by the United States.

## F

FINALING—Last minute missile preparation, including such items as final inspection of safety wiring and connectors, conducted just before entering a countdown.

FIREX—The water supply system that can direct a stream in the engine area, should the launch attempt prove abortive.

FLIGHT READINESS FIRING (FRF)—A short duration test firing of the first stage engine sometimes performed prior to the launch.

## G

GANTRY—Service platforms elevated to various heights outside the missile and moved gantry-like on railroad tracks.

GRAVITATION—The attraction of all bodies in the universe for one another; this attraction is in direct proportion to the product of the masses of the bodies under consideration and varies inversely as the square of the distance between them.

GUIDED MISSILE—An unmanned vehicle whose trajectory is capable of being altered by a mechanism within the vehicle.

## H

HARDWARE—An all-encompassing term that refers to the component parts of a missile.

## I

ICBM—Intercontinental ballistic missile with a range of approximately 5,000 nautical miles (such as Atlas, Titan, and Minuteman).

IGNITE—To start the combustion process of a rocket engine.

IMPACT PREDICTOR—Range Safety device that shows the Range Safety Officer at any time during missile flight where the missile would impact should he command destruct at that instant.

INSTRUMENTATION—Monitoring devices attached to the missile that indicate (through radio in flight or wires before flight) the performance or condition of missile components.

INVERTER—An electrical device which converts missile battery power to higher voltage at the frequency appropriate to power missile electrical components.

IRBM—Intermediate range ballistic missile with a range of approximately 1,500 nautical miles (such as Thor, Polaris, and Jupiter).

## L

LAUNCHER—The structure that carries or holds the missile during pre-flight preparation and launch.

LIFT OFF—The instant at which thrust equals weight and forward motion starts.

LOX—Liquid oxygen.

LUNAR PROBE—A firing which has as its major objectives experiments associated with the moon.

# M

MAGNETIC FIELD—The magnetic lines of force that surround and move about the earth from north to south. Whether other planets have magnetic fields is not known.

MATE—To erect one missile stage upon another.

MICROMETEORITE—A dust-size meteor of unknown origin and speed.

MOCK COUNTDOWN—A countdown rehearsal usually complete except for loading propellants and firing the engine.

# O

ORBIT—The path of revolution of one heavenly body around another.

OUTER SPACE—The vast reaches of space beyond the influence of the earth.

# P

PAD—The launch area.

PAYLOAD—The package of scientific instruments boosted by the missile.

PIONEER—The code name applied to the series of space probes conducted by the United States. Pioneer I launched October 11, 1958, the second U.S.A.F. lunar probe attempt.

PROGRAMMING—A series of pitch turns used to direct the missile properly during its power-on flight.

PROJECT COMMAND—The commanding team of the countdown, the ultimate decision-making authority.

PROJECT ENGINEER—The engineer charged with the responsibility of consolidating and coordinating all aspects of a project, of insuring that the design and flight meet the requirements of the customer.

# R

RADAR PLOT—A real-time graph of the position of the missile derived from radar tracking data.

RADIATION—High energy sub-atomic particles or quanta traveling in space or captured by the gravitational or magnetic field of the earth. In another sense, the radio signals originating from the missile.

RANGE SAFETY—The group charged with responsibility for protecting life and property that might be endangered by an errant missile.

RE-ENTRY—The flight of a missile or payload back into the earth's atmosphere.

xvi

RETRO ROCKET—A forward directed rocket designed to slow down its carrier when fired.

## S

SATELLITE—A small planet or man-made body revolving around a mother planet.

SCANNING—Repeatedly surveying adjacent strips of the field of view to make up a composite picture.

SCRUB—Cancellation of a firing test.

SERVICE TOWER—The scaffold from which the missile is serviced when in a vertical position. See *gantry*.

SIGNAL STRENGTH—The strength or intensity of a radio signal measured at the receiver.

SPIN ROCKETS—Tangentially directed rockets designed to impart spin to the carrier.

STAGES—The individual and separable vehicles of a multi-stage rocket.

STAND FOG—The water supply at the launch stand which can spray the area with a fog or water mist in case of an abortive launch.

## T

TASK—An integrated unit of work or associated jobs to be accomplished during a countdown.

TASK LEADER—The engineer charged with the responsibility of accomplishing a task.

TELEMETRY—The missile-borne radio transmitting system that carries information derived from the missile instrumentation to ground receivers for recording and later analysis.

TERMINAL COUNT—The final thirty-five minutes of the countdown, during which all members of the firing team are in the block-house and the firing area is cleared.

TEST CONDUCTOR—The engineer responsible for coordinating the countdown and countdown activities leading to the firing of the missile.

THRUST—The propulsive force developed by a rocket engine.

TRACKING—Following the missile while in flight.

## V

VERNIER ROCKET—A low thrust rocket used to adjust the final velocity of the missile.

# FIRST INTO OUTER SPACE

Missile 127 blasts off on first space probe.

"Man stations for the terminal count."

I said the words quickly, almost automatically, and released the intercom key. It was Sunday, August 17, 1958,
6:29 A.M., but we were aware only of the seconds ticking
off the clocks along the wall before us. In just 600 seconds,
at T-35, the terminal countdown to outer space would begin.

In only 45 minutes from now, I thought, I would lift my
thumb and, if everything went well, man's first rocket to
the moon would lift into the heavens from this sand trap
called Cape Canaveral.

We were well into Year One of the Space Age. It started
in October of 1957 when the Russians sent an earth satellite into orbit. Our own satellite program had moved ahead
swiftly, and now we were ready to attempt an orbit of the
most intriguing objective of all—the moon. We were ready
to attempt man's first step into outer space. I was aware
of the lore of the moon, of the writings from early times,

of the pioneering work of rocket experts, scientists, mathematicians and astronomers and what this attempt would have meant to them; but I confess that as I stood in the blockhouse this day, my mind was only concerned with the business at hand.

Missilemen are creatures of habit. Now it was time to pull out a cigar, light it, savor every puff until T-9 minutes when the "no smoking" order went out over the public address system in the blockhouse. Then we reached for our white cotton shirts, pulled them on. Mine had large block letters across the back: TEST CONDUCTOR.

Miles Ross, of Space Technology Laboratories, the Test Director, faced me; near him stood Captain Brandy Griffith, of the Air Force, the Test Controller; with us also were Air Force Major Hal Myers and Dick Morrison, of Space Technology Laboratories. They talked in low whispers, and I thought I saw tension etched on their faces and wondered if the flip-flop of my stomach was visible on mine.

Bill Duval, the boss of Douglas Aircraft at Cape Canaveral, walked over. Bill considered himself a jinx and wouldn't stay in the blockhouse even during test firings of the Douglas Thor missile. This was the big one—and he was ready to leave now.

"Give her hell, Ted," he said.

I don't remember if I thanked him. My stomach muscles tightened; I bit into the end of the cigar. This was the moment. It was now or never, I said to myself.

"All personnel switch your intercom to facilities loop," I announced.

We were ready now. The heavy steel door at the rear

4

of the blockhouse slammed shut and it startled me—as always. It sounded like the rumble of an explosion outside on the launching pad on Complex 17-A. My eyes moved quickly to the television monitors which were our eyes on the pad. It was no explosion, I knew, for I could see the mighty 88-foot, four-stage moon vehicle sitting on the pad, frosted by the intense cold of the liquid oxygen inside it and glowing in the early morning sun.

The Timer picked up the countdown manual, and we gathered about the Project Command console. I watched the red second hand sweep around the face of a clock synchronized with WWV, the National Bureau of Standards international time reference.

"On my 'mark,'" I said, "we will begin counting at T minus thirty-five. Five, four, three, two, one—*mark!*"

"T minus thirty-five minutes—*mark*," the Timer called out.

We had begun the final countdown.

The Talker called out item by item the checks and the steps to be made to climax the countdown.

"Check payload ready."

The answer: "Ready."

"Able accelerometer heat on."

"On."

"Stand fog and deluge disable."

"Disable."

"Increase water pressure."

"Roger."

We were locked in the blockhouse and felt cut off from the rest of the world. We were aware of nothing outside except a missile and voices speaking to us on intercom loops.

5

But a mile behind us across the scrub grass a group of newsmen stood anxiously atop a support structure following the Timer's count. Now they had put aside their playing cards, had stopped their jokes, stood by telephones ready to flash the word of our success—or failure—around the world.

Three miles to the rear of us, in Central Control, the Superintendent of Range Operations and the Range Safety Officer tensely watched plotting boards and radar units, keeping their fingers crossed, hoping no aircraft would stray across our danger area, no shrimp boat would wander out on the Atlantic Missile Range. The SRO talked to Brandy Griffith every few minutes on the intercom, "You're clear now, Brandy. Looks good."

Atop Central Control, Major General Donald M. Yates, commanding general of the Air Force Missile Test Center; Major General Bernard A. Schriever, of the Air Force's Ballistic Missile Division; and Roy W. Johnson, director of the Advanced Research Projects Agency, listened to the countdown.

In Inglewood, California, technicians at the Data Reduction Center of Space Technology Laboratories were ready to receive information relayed from the missile tracking stations when the missile was launched.

In Santa Monica, California, officials at Douglas Aircraft, the airframe designer and Test Conductor for Project Able I, waited for some word.

In Manchester, England; Westford, Massachusetts; Hilo, Hawaii; and Singapore, radio telescope tracking stations were aimed at the skies listening for the payload.

6

Missile 127 on launching pad.

And at Cocoa Beach, Florida, just a few miles away from Cape Canaveral, thousands of men, women, and children stood near their cars, some with telescopes and field glasses, watching Complex 17-A, waiting for the moment when the missile would blast off. The most curious had waited all night, for the rumor-wise seemed to know we were going to fire at dawn.

The Timer continued his unemotional calling-off of the minutes. The Talker read his items and the engineers reported the results.

Now we had reached 60 seconds. I twisted and untwisted the wire on my headset. Now was the time. Nothing can go wrong, I told myself, not believing it but trying to convince myself. Now we were within a minute of man's first attempt to go within the vicinity of the moon.

"T-sixty seconds . . . *mark.*"

"Telemetry internal."

"Internal."

"Charts high speed."

"High speed."

"Check all batteries."

"Roger."

"T minus fifty seconds . . . *mark.*"

"Close LOX bleed valves."

"Closed."

"Arm."

"Armed."

"Able power to lock up."

"Roger."

"T minus forty seconds . . . *mark.*"

9

"Check inverter."

"Good."

"Able to ready."

"Ready."

"T minus thirty seconds . . . *mark.*"

"Start tanks."

"Pressurized."

"Open vernier fuel vent."

"Open."

"Check arm."

"Armed."

"Twenty seconds . . . T minus ten seconds."

"Nine-eight-seven-six-five-four-three."

Joe Broadbent looked my way. My thumb was up. "Two-one-zero, ignition." Then he pressed the launch button.

I looked up at the television screen. The missile stood there. Then there was a flash as the small vernier rockets fired. It seemed minutes before there was a large flash, accompanied by smoke and flame—and the Rocketdyne engine in the Thor had ignited.

The missile did not move. My breath stopped coming.

Go, go, go. Move, move, move now, I cried to the missile, but the words were deep inside me.

Then it seemed to waver on the stand, then it lifted, ever so slowly, up—slowly up, slowly, slowly.

I heard someone yell out, "Go, baby, go."

Someone else cried, "Go, you bastard, go, go!"

It continued to rise. The television screen covered only one slightly blurred missile length. Now the screen emp-

Launching of Lunar Probe No. 1.

tied as the rocket rose out of television view, and we knew it was on its way.

Cheers broke out, and there was disorder and noise in the blockhouse. Tensions were momentarily relieved. It was going.

But we were still an operating team. There were still things to secure, even though the main job was now that of the tracking stations, Range Safety in Central Control, and Data Reduction.

I heard the Timer calling out the plus seconds and the Talker going about his task as the pad secured. ". . . T plus ten seconds. . . ."

"Firex on."

"Deflector water off."

Outside it was a warm morning and only a few pale wisps of clouds marred the naked blue sky. The sun was high and orange, the kind you see on Japanese calendars.

The moon rocket continued to climb straight up, trailing behind it a bright white flame, and on the ground smoke wrapped itself around the water-soaked launching pad.

Then the missile turned slightly toward the sea, to the north of east, and appeared well on its way. The Superintendent of Range Operations talked to Griffith on the intercom. We heard him say, "Looking good, Brandy. . . ."

The deafening roar of the mighty booster engine died in the blockhouse. The missile was 50 seconds up now and a vapor trail followed it. We listened for reports. The missile continued to climb. "It's on course, Brandy, it's on course."

Have we done it? I asked myself. It seemed incredible, but this man-made rocket, carrying an 85-pound payload of scientific instruments, was on its way to outer space—space which was only a far-off dream a few years ago.

*Had we actually done it?* Someone shook my hand. Someone else patted me on the back. I looked at the others. They were watching telemetry at our receiving stations, and I looked skyward but could only see the cabled roof of the blockhouse.

Out over the Atlantic, miles up, there was a puff of smoke. Was it the second stage starting? No, it was too early for that. It was an explosion at 77 seconds—and the dream had ended.

I first heard of the proposed lunar probes over a plate of enchilada con huevo at the Casa Escobar in West Los Angeles toward the end of 1957. I had been at Cape Canaveral, Florida, working with the Douglas Aircraft Company team on the Thor intermediate range ballistic missile, which we were testing for the Air Force. This was a production-line item at Douglas' Santa Monica plant, and I had been called back to the home base for a conference.

Jim Gunkel, an old friend, who headed the aero-astrodynamics section of the missiles and space systems engineering department of Douglas, asked me to go to lunch at a favorite spot, the Casa Escobar on Pico Boulevard, three miles from the plant. The restaurant is white adobe with a red-clay tile roof. The front door of the picturesque little place is heavy oak with an old-fashioned, black Spanish doorknob. The rooms are

15

dimly lit, and most of the booths have wood seats which get tiresome after an hour of sitting. But we liked the atmosphere, the Mexican waiters, and the food.

Jim, a baby elephant of a man with a good sense of humor and a strong devotion to his job, ordered his favorite, enchilada and a chili relleno. The meal started out as purely a personal and social affair, for none of us talked of company projects away from the plant.

However, Jim got around to the subject of countdowns, the sequence of events which lead up to a missile launching.

"Ted," he finally said, "I wonder if you could run a countdown in such a way that it would end up at a particular time."

My first reaction to his statement—for I didn't take it as a question—was to say that such a thing was almost an impossibility. A countdown is a pretty complex business, a series of events which follow in sequence, hundreds of items to check, and any one may give trouble. They follow one after another in a system of checks and rechecks, the closing of one valve, the opening of others, turning this knob, setting that gauge and regulating this device, seemingly ad infinitum.

In the early stages of missile development, countdowns may be largely unpredictable. In the development program we had an estimated firing time, and we knew how long our countdown should take with no troubles. But development countdowns were designed to uncover troubles, or, at least, potential troubles, *before* flight. If a question arose about any one of a thou-

16

sand items, we had to stop and convince ourselves that everything was O.K. Sometimes that led to "scrubbing" (stopping) a test, and cost days. In our countdowns, we started with item No. 1 and fired only after all items had been checked.

Jim and I knew that it would be almost impossible to predict the troubles which might be encountered, and to fire at a particular time we had to be almost certain of a trouble-free missile. We were in a program of testing and evaluation, and we were not working with completely predictable equipment. There were other imponderables, too, for we fired on Cape Canaveral's Atlantic Missile Range, and the range had to be clear before a missile could be fired safely. Systems over which we had no control, such as the range safety tracking radars, had to work perfectly and be ready when the missile was.

I gulped my beer and contemplated Jim's proposal, thinking that here was a strange question. Imagine trying to fire a missile at, say, 12 noon of a designated day. When would you start the countdown? How could you end up on the minute?

As the conversation progressed, Jim leaned across the table and said that his people were looking into trajectories for a lunar payload. In order to do the job with the Thor, he said, the Thor would probably have to be lightened, the guidance system removed and two or three stages would have to be added, plus a payload.

There it was. Going to the moon over a plate of enchiladas. It was unreal. You just don't sit in a little

17

Mexican restaurant, eating, drinking beer and casually saying, "We want to go to the moon." Here, in this incongruous setting, I realized, we were talking seriously about man's first venture into outer space.

Would I be asked to run the countdowns to the moon?

The thought frightened me at first—*and I mean frightened*. As a Test Conductor, when you are in charge of a countdown, it is difficult to be a hero, but one mistake, one error in judgment, and you are a bum. In a lunar probe mission, the usual responsibilities would be magnified, the pressure multiplied a hundred-fold. I recalled many of the early missile countdowns, the successes and also the failures, and the terrible tensions of even "normal" missile firings.

But I realized, too, that perhaps I was to be given an opportunity to contribute in some way to one of man's boldest undertakings. And this would be not a military test, but a peaceful, purely scientific exploration. The idea pushed my imagination to its limits—and I knew I wanted very badly to be a part of it.

Forgetting my lunch, I listened as Jim talked. Some planning already had gone on at a much higher level between the Advanced Research Projects Agency, the Air Force's Ballistic Missile Division, and officials of the International Geophysical Year. Douglas was engaged in theoretical studies of hardware and trajectories, and the government agencies were considering the use of our Thor for the first stage. As we talked, we both knew we had the potential to do the job. We thought we

18

were capable of doing what man had longed to do since the beginning of time.

Jim asked me again, "Do you think we can run a countdown so that we can fire at a particular time?"

I didn't know. I shook my head. I asked what the time limitations would be. He wasn't sure, but he knew they would be short and confining. The moon is in proper position for a probe only on certain days, even minutes, of the month, but he couldn't yet tell me whether we would be asked to fire within a few minutes or a few hours of a particular time.

The whole idea was kept under wraps within our company, but Jim asked that I look at the problem as soon as I got back to Canaveral. We left the restaurant, walked out into the bright sun, and I remember looking up at the sky as if to say, "We're coming."

Lunar Probe Countdown

When I got back to Cape Canaveral from my West Coast meeting with Jim Gunkel, I really got to work. We had a big job to do—we had to develop a new countdown format which would permit us to fire at an exact predetermined time of day. A countdown on a lunar probe project might be different from the usual countdown format. It was a real challenge.

The first order of business was to analyze our past Thor countdowns to find out what was causing our holds. During countdowns we think in terms of time remaining until firing. This, in a sense, produces a sort of "backwards" time; in fact, in the blockhouse we have a clock with a counterclockwise face. Let's say that our desired firing time is 11 P.M. and our countdown is expected to take five hours. We start making our firing preparations at 6 P.M. Any troubles that might extend the duration of the countdown beyond five hours would

21

extend the countdown past the 11 P.M. deadline, or firing time. Whenever we have troubles that cause us to delay our scheduled countdown activities we stop our backwards clock. This is a hold. When our troubles are fixed or explained and we are back into the countdown, we start the backwards clock again, or "release the hold."

Since we knew that in a lunar probe the optimum firing time would probably be tightly confined to a few minutes, it was extremely important for us to study the simple Thor experience to learn all we could about holds: what caused them, when they occurred, and how long they lasted.

In a normal development countdown with a Thor missile, holds could be minutes or hours long. After releasing a hold, we would proceed with the next steps in the countdown. Our holds in nonlunar shots simply delayed our firing time. However, this could not be the case in the lunar probes. We guessed that our allowable tolerance in firing would be fifteen to twenty minutes, but, no matter what the time interval, we knew that our research would have to result in a format that would take into account all the variables, all the possible hold situations, and still get us to ignition at just the right minute.

The trick was not merely to obtain a particular velocity but also to achieve an exact firing time, which, when wedded to trajectory and velocity, would allow our vehicle to "meet" the moon, make a junction with it at a predetermined point in space. Back at Cape

Canaveral my colleagues and I drew freely on expert advice and the records of the Atlantic Missile Range and our associate contractors. We started to develop a countdown procedure which would end at a given minute. The countdown would be one of the keys to the moon.

The Cape Canaveral dateline was already famous. But the words "Cape Canaveral" have been translated to mean much more than they actually imply. The Cape itself is but one part of a large complex and is simply the missile launching site.

Cape Canaveral is a part of the Air Force Missile Test Center under command of Major General Donald M. Yates. The Center consists of these component parts, all under the Air Research and Development Command of the Air Force: the headquarters, which is Patrick Air Force Base and houses research and military areas; Cape Canaveral itself, which is the launching site; and the Atlantic Missile Range. The Atlantic Missile Range extends 5,000 miles to the southeast and includes a series of tracking stations located on a string of islands along the range.

Other tracking stations also come under the Air Force Missile Test Center: some stations on the Florida coast and some ocean-going vessels and aircraft.

The Air Force Missile Test Center is the largest ballistic- and cruise-type missile proving ground in the free world.

The Air Force Missile Test Center—Patrick Air Force Base, Cape Canaveral, the Atlantic Missile Range—does

23

not build missiles; it provides location and services for flight-testing them.

When United States military leaders became increasingly interested in missiles in the closing days of World War II, a program of research and development was started, but no suitable missile-testing range was available. Instrument ranges were available at Point Mugu and Inyokern, California, and we had a range at White Sands, New Mexico, but none of these were adequate for the missiles conceived in the minds of the military. In 1946 a search was begun for a suitable long-distance range in the United States, and Cape Canaveral was selected for a long-range missile launching site, with a proposed flight-test range to extend in a southeasterly direction over the South Atlantic Ocean.

Cape Canaveral was an ideal location: it was isolated and it was already partly owned by the government. The facilities of the nearby Banana River Naval Air Station could be converted to supply logistic, technical, and administrative support. This air station later became Patrick Air Force Base.

Plans called for long-range missiles, and in this application a firing range starting at Canaveral had an advantage over all other locations surveyed. Missiles could be fired on a range down the South Atlantic which did not pass over the major shipping lanes of the world and but a few large land masses. Moreover, islands in the West Indies and the South Atlantic offered ideal locations for permanent stations required to track missiles in flight and to record performance data transmitted from them.

Negotiations were started with the British for construction of missile tracking stations on various British-controlled islands, and by May 1949 legislation was passed approving the construction. Already the Navy had transferred the Banana River Air Station to the Air Force and it had been renamed Patrick Air Force Base. Work had already begun on the construction of launching and telemetry facilities needed at the Cape.

The program got under way quickly. The first missile launching from the Cape occurred on July 24, 1950, when a German V-2 rocket, carrying a second-stage Army WAC Corporal missile in its nose, was successfully launched. It set the world's altitude record, 250 miles, which stood for years.

In February of 1951 construction started on the first down-range tracking station at Grand Bahama Island. That June the Air Force launched its Matador missile, the first operational surface-to-surface missile.

By 1957 agreements had been concluded with Great Britain, as well as with the Dominican Republic and Brazil, establishing all of the twelve major tracking stations we now have in operation. In addition, a number of ocean-going vessels were modified to serve as floating telemetry stations between the tracking station at St. Lucia Island and the terminal point of the Atlantic Missile Range, Ascension Island. There are also twelve small stations along the Florida coast.

The United States had organized the Test Center

25

and a string of islands for tracking stations. The tracking stations, however, must be maintained. The Air Force had often used private enterprise in nonmilitary operations. It was decided that much of the maintenance operation of the Air Force Missile Test Center could best be maintained by private enterprise.

In 1954 bids were requested for operation of the Cape Canaveral launching site and the Atlantic Missile Range. Pan American World Airways, with much experience in operation of overseas bases, received the contract and subcontracted with the Radio Corporation of America for the technical work involved in the operation and maintenance of the range. Visitors to the Cape Canaveral launching site are often surprised to see, instead of helmeted, gun-toting men of the Air Force, neat, blue-uniformed guards with "PAA" patches on their clothing.

The missile contractors needed space at Cape Canaveral to assemble and test their missile and the component parts which they are developing. For example, Douglas occupies two hangars, "M" and "L," in the industrial area where we work on the Thor. At Complex 17, three miles away, we have more shops, two launch pads, and a blockhouse.

Three miles to the rear of the complexes is Central Control. The range clearance and in-flight safety functions are performed in Central Control and contact is maintained with all the tracking stations. Central Control also O.K.s the time of firings, clears the range and

26

monitors the whole operation to be sure desired range instrumentation will be available.

Our research into a new countdown technique did not consume all of our time. The Thor missile was still in the research and development stage, and we were firing the Thor down the Atlantic Missile Range with regularity and success.

The lunar probe shots—if they materialized for us— were not to be our first special project either. During this time we were also concerned with the Able program. The Air Force wanted a series of nose-cone re-entry tests at long range, and the Able program saw us using two stage vehicles with the Thor as the first stage. These firings got a great deal of publicity because we carried mice in several of the nose cones. These tests were directly related to our proposed lunar probe work because the configuration of the first and second stages of the missiles used in the Able re-entry tests could be virtually the same as we would use in the lunar probes. In the lunar program a third stage and payload would probably be carried in place of the Able nose cone.

This remained to be seen.

# CHAPTER 3

Jim Gunkel had tossed me a dream. He had whetted my appetite. Although I was actively engaged in other projects, the lunar probe idea was constantly on my mind. I had been working with the Thor, a military weapon, and I liked the idea that I might be involved in the excitement and discovery of the unknown in a space exploration project.

Space study and the idea of space exploration in this country were at first purposely kept nonmilitary in order to prevent the dilution of the ballistic missile development tests with "side jobs." It was feared by top officials that a space program based on ballistic missiles would delay the primary job of producing a deterrent weapon. Furthermore, we had agreed with the rest of the world to make our initial space exploration efforts part of the International Geophysical Year program. This required that we publish all the data col-

28

lected. We did not particularly relish publishing details about our ballistic missiles. So the decision was made to develop Vanguard under Naval Research labs. This missile was to be independent of our ballistic missile effort and was not to draw on Thor, Jupiter, Titan, or Atlas.

As in any new development program, we had our troubles and delays. It all seemed worth while though; we were on the threshold of space. Then, on October 4, 1957, Russia launched her Sputnik I. There had been some indications that such a launching was imminent, but these were not widely appreciated. The world was electrified by the news of the Russian success. The satellite weighed 184 pounds as compared to the top weight of 20 pounds of the Vanguard payload. We had hardly recovered from the first stunning news when Russia did it again, and Sputnik II, weighing six times as much as Sputnik I, hurtled through space. This time the Russians had a live dog in the payload and the world hardly believed the news.

The eyes of the world were on Canaveral on December 6, 1957. The United States was going to try a Vanguard shot. Up and down the Florida coast the beaches were crowded. The representatives of Associated Press and United Press International had set up shop on Cocoa Beach, along with representatives of *Time, Life, Newsweek*, the *New York Times, Wall Street Journal* and the fast-growing new space magazines. Television and radio stations gave hourly reports on "progress." No previous missile firing had attracted such attention. Russia had put two satellites into orbit in space and they were beeping their way around earth. Now it was our turn. The tension must have been great for the Martin and Navy Vanguard team. The Russians, with no prior announcements and most likely no announcement at all if they had failed in their attempts, had worked, apparently, in an atmosphere free of tension and pressures created by glaring publicity.

America was keenly interested in the Vanguard team. I was parked about three miles from the launching pad, and I could hear the countdown on the Cape's public address system. I also turned on my radio and listened to a local station covering the shoot.

"Three, two, one, zero."

The missile fired, rose slightly, and then it was suddenly engulfed in a bright orange fireball. We couldn't believe it. The announcer didn't understand what he saw. He said, "There's the engine flame. She should start to rise any second now." But she never did.

After this failure Washington authorized the Army Ballistic Missile Agency to launch a satellite using its short-range ballistic missile, the Redstone, as a booster. This marked the first application of a military weapon to the country's space program. The Army was successful on its first satellite launching attempt, and on January 31, 1958, the United States had a satellite in orbit.

We had always assumed the government would eventually go to its ballistic missile arsenal for hardware; our only question was when. Ballistic missile technology, after all, is space technology. An intercontinental ballistic missile, such as the Atlas or the Titan, for instance, spends 90 per cent of its flight time above the sensible atmosphere—in space. Ballistic missiles do not depend on the atmosphere to sustain them in flight but rather follow elliptical paths like bullets. The energy derived from their propellants is expended quickly and is transformed into velocity. The rocket engine performs this transformation, the pressure within the combustion chamber acting against the forward end of the rocket engine to develop thrust. This force, pushing against the mass of the missile, accelerates it to higher and higher speeds. As the fuel is consumed the mass of the missile decreases and the rocket thrust produces ever-increasing acceleration. When the propellants are exhausted the speed of the missile is high enough to send the payload on a gracefully arching course toward the target. In a multi-stage missile the second-stage engine takes over after the first is exhausted and adds its energy-velocity to that already generated by the first stage. These concepts are true whether the missile is pushing a nuclear warhead or the upper stages of a deep-space probe.

The Thor intermediate range ballistic missile would be ideal for such space exploration.

Early in January of 1958, after my return from California, we received a teletype message from Jack Bromberg, the chief project engineer for Thor, saying that he and other top brass would come to Patrick the following week to join in a series of briefings which had been set up by the Air Force Ballistic Missile Division on the Able series. The purpose of these briefings was to acquaint the range with new requirements of the Able re-entry project.

Before we joined the Ballistic Missile Division people at the base that January morning to co-ordinate plans for the Able project, we had what we called an "in-house" meeting at Douglas House, a large, open, patio-type Spanish structure in a grove of palm and pine trees on the ocean's edge at Cocoa Beach, just off Highway AIA between Canaveral and Patrick Air Force Base. Douglas leased this house in the early days to provide sleeping quarters for visiting firemen. Douglas House was our off-hours headquarters.

I remember the meeting well. It was held in the early morning hours. The meeting at the base was scheduled to start at nine and the Douglas House session at seven-thirty. When I drove up to the house the sun was coming up over a cold, barren sea and the mist was lying close to the ground. From the front windows of the house you can see nothing but the vast expanse of the sea ahead of you and, to the left, a thin strip of land which was Cape Canaveral, some seven miles across the water and jutting out like a finger into the Atlantic. The red lights on the gantries (service towers) at Canaveral remind you that the apparent calm is deceptive and the future still has a story to tell.

We discussed the current Able program. It was a quiet and orderly meeting, and the sound of the ocean made a soft rhythmic background for us. This was part of the Douglas team that would labor over the advancing Thor missile, the special Able re-entry projects and, ultimately, the lunar probes.

The meeting was held in January, during that period of time when the American public was discouraged over our space attempts and still a bit stunned over the Russian successes. The Russians had two satellites, Sputniks I and II, to their credit, while we had nothing to show the world for our attempts. The Army had not yet attempted their satellite launch.

We knew the lunar probe attempts were at least six months, possibly even a year, away. The Russians, fired by their great successes, could be thinking of a lunar probe as their next coup. We were not engaged in a race, but American prestige was at low ebb and a first in any phase of space exploration was needed to counter-act Russian political and propaganda advantages.

Lunar probe talk was discussed by only a few of us at this meeting. It had not been announced officially and only a handful of Douglas people were in on the possibility. We could not talk about it outside this group. And, besides, we still had the Able re-entry tests to face, which were exciting and demanding in them-selves. The countdown studies were going on, but we had nothing definite to shoot for as far as dates were concerned.

The first official statement about America's—and the world's—initial lunar probes came on March 27, 1958, from Secretary of Defense Neil H. McElroy. McElroy reported that, with the approval of the President, the Advanced Research Projects Agency of the Defense

33

Department would proceed with several programs for launching a number of small unmanned space vehicles.

The authorized programs included both the launching of scientific earth satellites and lunar probes designed to determine our capacity for exploring space in the vicinity of the moon and to provide a closer look at the moon. Roy W. Johnson, Advanced Research Projects Agency director, issued instructions to the three branches of the armed services: the Air Force Ballistic Missile Division, headed by Major General Bernard A. Schriever, was to conduct three lunar probes; the Army's Ballistic Missile Agency at Huntsville, Alabama, was to conduct two lunar probes; the Navy was to develop a mechanical ground-scanning system for use in the probes.

The satellite attempts would be further efforts to learn, through a space technique, more about the planet earth, the upper atmosphere, and the doorstep of space, while the lunar probe attempts would be man's first attempt to explore the areas beyond the earth and earth's region of immediate influence.

The earth satellite, such as the Army satellite, was still an earthbound experiment which could orbit at altitudes from a hundred or so miles up to one or two thousand miles. The lunar probes, on the other hand, were planned to go into outer space—to leave the earth and never return.

We had demonstrated that we could match the Russians in getting an earth satellite up and into orbit around the earth; could we get a lunar probe vehicle into outer space and into orbit around the moon?

The lunar probes were to be a part of the International Geophysical Year program sponsored by the National Academy of Sciences with the support of the National Science Foundation. Data resulting from these probes would be transmitted, the statement added, to the Academy's IGY Committee for sharing with other IGY nations according to IGY policies.

(On October 1, 1958, President Eisenhower transferred from the Advance Research Projects Agency to the newly created National Aeronautics and Space Administration—NASA—control of the second and third lunar probe attempts.)

Now in March, Major General Schriever reiterated an earlier statement of his, saying that the Air Force could initiate an astronautic development program "with no dilution or diversion of our ballistic missile program." He said, "We have a vast military, scientific and industrial organization experienced in the design, development, testing and production of ballistic missiles. Moreover, this organization is staffed by personnel of the greatest competence who have mastered many new fields of knowledge which can be springboards to substantial short cuts in our mastery of astronautics."

The objectives of the first flight test of the Air Force's lunar vehicle were: (1) to achieve proper powered flight performance from the three stages of the test vehicle; (2) to reach escape velocity from the earth's gravitational field (This objective was somewhat misleading, since in the trajectory finally chosen the payload would

35

not exceed escape velocity.); (3) to obtain data, using the special tracking stations developed for the lunar probe program, during the flight of the test vehicle out of the earth's gravitational field and into space to a distance of approximately 250,000 miles from earth; (4) to achieve trajectory control sufficient to place the payload in the vicinity of the moon.

Secretary McElroy stated at the time that odds of success were one in ten. He was probably being optimistic. He also pointed out what Gunkel had told me months before, that a great deal of computer study would be required in order to specify the most favorable launch time. These unique launch requirements would necessitate a major change in the normal countdown procedure. These problems licked, it was still necessary for the vehicle itself, with new stages, to perform properly.

It was also at this time, in March of 1958, that McElroy announced that the first test vehicle of the lunar probe series would consist of a Thor intermediate range ballistic missile as the first, or booster, stage; a highly modified second stage developed by Space Technology Laboratories (now working on the hardware itself in addition to its scientific advisory role to the Air Force) and propelled by a version of Aerojet-General's second-stage Vanguard engine; and a solid propellant third stage developed for an advanced version of the Vanguard by the Allegheny Ballistics Laboratory; plus a payload stage.

At this point the Thor was still in its research and de-

First or "booster" stage of the space probe vehicle—a Douglas built THOR
Intermediate Range Ballistic Missile—shown in position at Cape Canaveral.

velopment stage, although we had repeatedly fired the missile in spectacular flight tests.

It was official now. Our baby, the Thor IRBM, would be part of the first lunar probe vehicle. We took great pride in this. We wanted to be the first into outer space, and we wanted to show the world a touch of old American know-how.

Secretary McElroy made his public disclosures in March. Now the world knew we were in earnest about the lunar probes. On April 4 we received a teletype from Douglas, Santa Monica: the code name for the lunar probes would be Project Able-I. We were in business; the project was rolling.

Santa Monica defined the missile configuration for us, we knew the telemetry assignments and the weight considerations. The missile was to enter our preparation and modification line in series with other Thors being prepared for flight testing. The hardware now began to arrive at Patrick and Canaveral for the lunar probe vehicle.

Rather unceremoniously, Missile 127 was being prepared in Hangar M. This would be the first lunar probe rocket, and we used to look at the white-painted bird and think, "What a job you've got ahead of you!" It moved from position to position, the modification jobs being done on schedule. Finally it was in the last hangar position where all the electrical systems were checked out prior to sending it to the pad. We knew its time was near.

In the meantime, our work on the countdown was

starting to crystallize. We reasoned that no matter how trouble-free the missile might be, holds still could not be eliminated. We could never anticipate delays caused by unpredictable events, such as shrimp boats wandering onto the range or a breakdown in communications between the Range Safety Officer and his forward observer. Our solution was to stretch out the countdown by inserting periods of "no work," or, if you will, built-in holds. In our first try at the lunar probe countdown, we scheduled in five hours of blank time, two hours after second-stage fueling, two hours at 135 minutes before firing and one hour at 35 minutes before firing. We decided, in effect, to lick the imponderables by letting them happen and using our blank periods to solve our problems. If this worked out, if we, or the range, could clear up our problems in the allotted "no work" time, we thought we could have a fair chance of firing at a specific time.

In June we received the DTO—Detailed Test Objectives—from the West Coast. This document defined the mission and described the trajectory for many of us for the first time. It was the first complete compilation of the flight plan. The DTO confirmed internal memoranda we had written defining the missile configuration and instrumentation assignments. It defined the complex series of events that had to occur in sequence after lift-off to send the payload on its way. Most important, it defined officially the acceptable launch dates and firing times in August. We had four consecutive days in which we might fire. The tolerance on our firing time

40

was to be fifteen to twenty minutes, depending on the firing day.

The hardware for the upper stages and the ground-support equipment was beginning to arrive now. New checkout gear had to be installed in the hangar, launcher, and blockhouse. We had to close Pad 17-A, where we flight-tested the Able missiles, for we had to change the gantry, or service tower, considerably to accommodate this new bird—an 88-foot-tall missile.

Ballistic Missile Division personnel agreed with our findings and plans on the countdown. Planning and range coordination was moving ahead in other areas, too. Lunar probe preparations were world-wide. The tracking stations were being set up. Communications links were being installed to the Trajectory and Data Reduction Center at Inglewood, California. Range Safety was preparing destruct curves indicating the allowable limits of trajectory dispersion over the range. If the vehicle wandered out of those limits it would be destroyed by a signal from Central Control. Even with a mission like this, safety on the range had to be preserved; our flight could not endanger life or property. All these activities had to be completed and all equipment had to be working two months from now at 7:14 A.M., August 17, 1958.

# CHAPTER 4

Hardware is no nickname. In the missile business you work with what we call hardware in the strictest meaning of the term. It is no slang, no nickname, no cute expression.

We were busily putting the hardware together at Cape Canaveral now. The work had begun in earnest on the Able-I project, the lunar probe.

Time has a habit of running away from you. It was running full tide now. Sputnik I had been launched on October 4, 1957; Sputnik II on November 3, 1957; I had talked with Gunkel the first of December, 1957; then I witnessed the Vanguard attempt on December 6; we had our Douglas House meeting at Canaveral early in January, 1958, and talked briefly on the lunar probe project; the Army's Redstone put a satellite in orbit on January 31; the Vanguard was highly successful March 17 with a satellite which would remain up for 2,000 years or more; and the public learned of the lunar probes on March 27.

Now it was June. We would fire in August.

The new lunar missile would be fired with no previous flight testing since it was the first of its kind. It was ticklish business, tricky, difficult and loaded with problems. We had to put together hardware which would kick the payload stage 24,000 miles an hour on a trajectory as carefully calculated as any computation in all history. When the launch button is pushed, 300,000 parts are dependent on one another. Not only must hundreds function properly while in flight but their sequence has to be started within minutes of a small time span—fifteen to twenty minutes on a particular morning in August. More than that—the firing range and the tracking stations spread over the world have to be ready in the same time interval.

Missiles are vastly complex, and this complexity is occasionally their undoing. Each system must work, each component part must function when commanded. A missile flight test seldom fails because of a basic inadequacy in design; usually a two-bit part fails, a seemingly insignificant link in a basically strong chain. To find the bugs before they can cause a flight failure, each design is tested repeatedly before it ever becomes a part of a missile. The parts must perform properly under test conditions more severe than the flight environment. They are heated, they are cooled, they are shaken at sea level and at simulated high altitude pressures; and, in some cases, literally hit with a sledge. The components are assembled into operating sub-systems and tested again. The individual sub-systems are plugged together to form larger complete systems and are tested yet again until finally the design is proved. This testing is usually done in the factories where the parts are made, and any failure or malfunction at this stage is cause for reviewing the design. Even after the design is established, individual production-line components are subjected to severe acceptance tests to show that they will perform properly.

Yet bugs may still remain. Flight testing is the final proof.

The preflight testing is not confined to actual flight components alone. Missile models are "flown" in wind tunnels to investigate aerodynamic performance, stability and control, and heating caused by air friction at high speeds. Able-I missiles were flown in quiet, air-conditioned rooms where the only sound was the clacking of automatic IBM typewriters. Digital computers at Space Technology Laboratories and at Douglas, Santa Monica, flew lunar trajectories using mathematical models of the Thor three-stage vehicle. They picked the exact time of launch and showed how much energy would be required to send the payload into orbit around the moon. The machines were supplied all the information affecting the real situation: the speed, size, and rotation of the earth; the motion of the moon, gravitational and atmospheric data; the missile turning program. The adjustable variables of the missile and of its launch were chosen in accordance with the computations of these

Profile of rocket power at rest shows THOR IRBM liquid propellant rocket engine manufactured by Rocketdyne.

FINAL ASSEMBLY

Testing of the main engine for the U.S.A.F. THOR
IRBM. Twin vernier engines are being fired.

machines. The mathematical missiles flew, just as surely as they were to fly in fact from Cape Canaveral, in the theoretical courses clicked out at Santa Monica and elsewhere. When all the parameters had been tentatively selected, final runs proved the ability of the vehicle. These runs had all the suspense of a real flight. Mathematicians, gathered around the machine's printout typewriter, cheered the theoretical payload on its way to the theoretical moon.

Possibly the most spectacular and crucial qualification tests were those performed on the mighty first-stage engines of the Thor. Rocketdyne, Inc., a division of North American Aviation, manufactures the engine. Engines are test fired by Rocketdyne at their Santa Susana, California test facility near the San Fernando Valley. The firings are conducted from well-protected control rooms carved in the hills. Each engine is run at full thrust before being shipped to Douglas for assembly in the airframe. Remote television cameras and recording instrumentation in the control room watch the engine electronically during its firing. The instrumentation permits final adjustment of this complex device and allows only acceptable units to pass on to flight missiles. When conditions are favorable, the low rumble of the firings can be heard across the valley.

The development of the Thor is a dramatic and magnificent achievement in itself. In November, 1955, the Department of Defense authorized the Air Force to develop an intermediate-range ballistic missile, a missile with a range of 1,500 miles. One month later contracts were let for the WS-315A weapon system, the Thor. The contract was signed with Douglas Aircraft on December 27, 1955. Douglas' job was defined as, ". . . Responsible for airframe fabrication, systems integration and ground-support equipment." In this assignment Douglas was to serve as the test conductor for the flight tests of the weapon system. The size and major characteristics of the missile were defined by an engineering team under the direction of chief project engineer J. L. (Jack) Bromberg (who came to be known as "Thorhead"), by the end of January, 1956. Bromberg is a man fiercely dedicated to his job, a hard-driving taskmaster who accepts no alibis, no excuses, no reasons why a task is not completed on time. He is not interested in problems, only results, and he pushes his men as he pushes himself. Thorhead gets results. The missile design was essentially complete by the end of July, 1956. The Air Force had its missile by the end of the year. All phases of the design proceeded in parallel. Manufacturing began even before the drawings were complete, and that manufacturing was begun on production tooling. Thor was a crash program.

The missile produced by this program was used as the first stage, or booster, of the moon rocket. The Thor is a beautiful and graceful beast, 62 feet tall. Most of its length is devoted to propellant tanks to carry the fuel and liquid oxygen. In the lunar probe version, the inertial guidance system built by AC Spark Plug was removed to lighten the load. Ballistic missile-type guidance was not needed in this mission, only proper aiming.

First stage (THOR) goes from hangar to gantry.

The Rocketdyne power plant for the Thor is a complex and efficient rocket engine developing 150,000 pounds of thrust. The engine was derived from a basic design used in the Atlas and Navaho programs. This permitted rapid development and in June, 1956, the first engine was delivered for the first Thor.

The Ordnance Division of the Food Machinery and Chemical Corp., at San Jose, California, produced the complete launcher and transporter-erector for the Thor weapon system. While not a part of the lunar probe program, Food Machinery, as subcontractor to Douglas for these parts, materially contributed to rapid Thor weapon development. Their production equipment was delivered two months ahead of schedule, in a total elapsed time of eight months from contract to hardware.

To complete the picture of Thor, General Electric's Missile and Ordnance Systems Department of Philadelphia produced the nose cone for the weapon system. In the lunar probe shots this payload was replaced by a second and a third stage to boost an instrumentation package into space.

The Thor program is managed by a three-part team composed of the Air Force Ballistic Missile Division, formerly commanded by Major General Schriever; the Ballistic Missile Office (now Center) of the Air Materiel Command; and Space Technology Laboratories. The Ballistic Missile Division has the over-all management responsibility for Air Force ballistic missile programs in this country. The Ballistic Missile Office is responsible

51

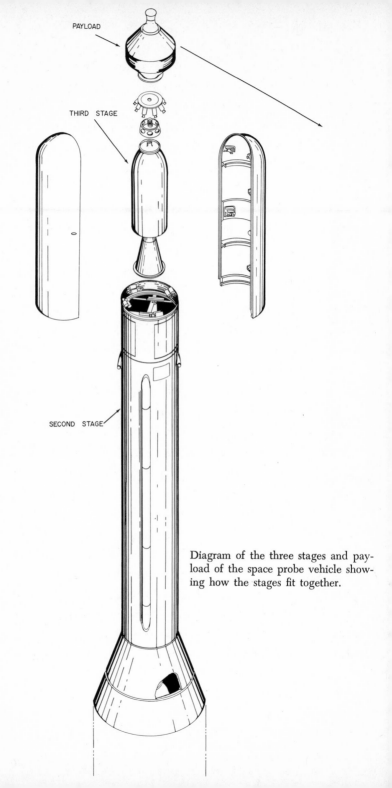

PAYLOAD

THIRD STAGE

SECOND STAGE

Diagram of the three stages and payload of the space probe vehicle showing how the stages fit together.

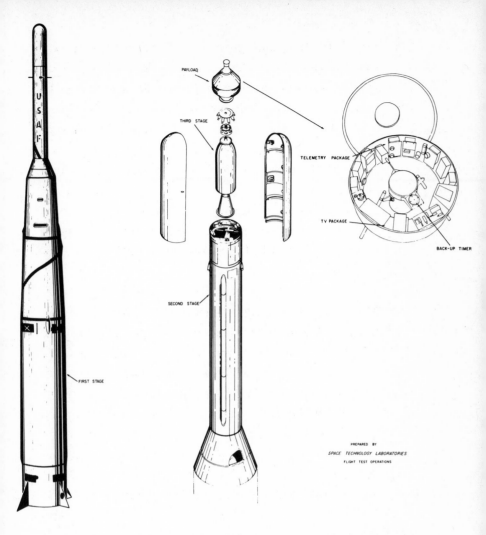

PAYLOAD

THIRD STAGE

TELEMETRY PACKAGE

TV PACKAGE

BACK-UP TIMER

SECOND STAGE

FIRST STAGE

U
S
A
F

PREPARED BY

*SPACE TECHNOLOGY LABORATORIES*

FLIGHT TEST OPERATIONS

Diagram of the stages of the space probe
vehicle with internal detail of payload.

for contracting and procurement. Space Technology Laboratories acts as a consultant to the Air Force, providing technical direction and scientific supervision. In the Able-I program another department of the Space Technology Laboratories had the responsibility for procuring and integrating the upper stage hardware which made up the vehicle which the Thor was to boost into outer space.

The new vehicle for shooting for the moon was to be made up of four stages. The Thor was the first stage: a modified Thor IRBM, specially lightened and instrumented.

The second stage was a modified version of the Navy Vanguard second-stage rocket, powered by an Aerojet-General liquid-fueled engine. The propellants were UDMH (unsymmetric dimethly hydrazene) and nitric acid, a combination which ignites spontaneously. This stage was about 19 feet long, 32 inches in diameter. It weighed two tons fueled, and its engine produced 7,500 pounds of thrust.

The third stage was a solid propellent rocket, manufactured by Allegheny Ballistics Laboratory. It weighed 500 pounds, was just five feet long and 18 inches in diameter. It developed 2,500 pounds of thrust. This stage and the payload were covered by an aerodynamic nose fairing which was to be jettisoned after the first and second stages separated.

The fourth stage was the payload. While the configuration and instrumentation varied slightly between shots, basically it consisted of two parts: the terminal

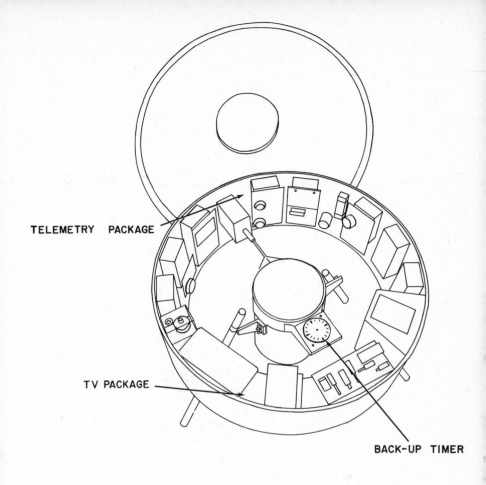

TELEMETRY PACKAGE

TV PACKAGE

BACK-UP TIMER

Diagram of internal detail of payload close up.

# PIONEER 2
# PAYLOAD PKG.

COSMIC RAY TELESCOPE

ION CHAMBER

BATTERY PACK

MULTIPLEXER AMPLIFIER

100 MW TELEMETRY TRANSMITTER

S.C.O. CHANNELS 1 & 6

BATTERY PACK

S.C.O. CHANNELS 2 & 3

MICROMETEORITE ELECTRONIC

S.C.O. CHANNEL 4

BATTERY PACK

MICRO METEORITE MICROPHONE

MAGNETOMETER COIL

MAGNETOMETER ELECTRONICS

BATTERY PACK

FILTERS

BATTERY PACK

SQUIB BATTERY PACK

MULTIPLEXER

RECEIVER RELAY BATTERY PACK

300 MW TELEMETRY & DOPPLER TRANSMITTER

FILTERS & DIPLEXER

COMMAND RECEIVER

ANTENNA GROUND PLANE

ANTENNA DIPOLE

BATTERY PACK FOR TV

T V ELECTRONICS

DAMPER RING

BATTERY PACK

COSMIC RAY MULTIPLEXER

S.C.O. CHANNEL 5

TV TELESCOPE

Interior of a payload stage, "Pioneer".

(or retro) rocket and the package of scientific instruments. It weighed about 85 pounds. The retro rocket had a thrust of 3,000 pounds—thrust used to "brake" it in the vicinity of the moon so that the payload might have the best chance of going into orbit around the moon. Eight small, solid propellent vernier rockets were attached to the base of the payload to be fired on radio command from the earth. These verniers would introduce final velocity correction, if needed, immediately after third-stage burnout. The instrumentation package included batteries, two telemetry systems and an electronic scanning device—a sort of television which could have provided the first indication of what to expect of the other side of the moon. The telemetry measurements included meteorite impact detection, the earth-moon magnetic field, total radiation encountered, compartment temperature and chamber pressure of the retro rocket.

The payload casing was made of Fiberglas and shaped liked two deep pie plates placed rim to rim. The package was one and a half feet long and 29 inches in diameter. The loaded payload was precisely balanced by counterweights. A complex pattern of alternately light and dark spaces over the surface of the shell was designed to control internal temperature in outer space where the heat of the sun and the cold of nothingness fight an eternal battle.

The payload package was assembled at Inglewood, California, under conditions which would have made the average operating room look dirty. These surgical precautions were taken so that the moon would remain uncontaminated in the improbable event of an impact on its surface. These precautions were continued throughout preparation at the Missile Test Center and launcher checkout.

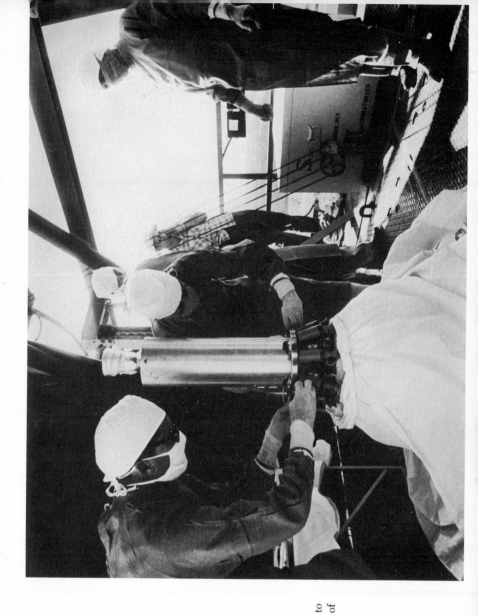

Attaching the vernier rockets to the payload stage, "Pioneer," of the space probe vehicle.

# CHAPTER 5

The Able-I project, the lunar probe, would be, as far as we knew, man's first attempt to send a vehicle from the surface of the earth into space toward the moon. The boys on the West Coast told us *how* the rocket was to get to the moon; our job was to get it ready and fire it at the right time. As the data and trajectories started coming in, we studied them to learn about the complex problem of going from earth to moon and how our bird would solve it. Our flight plan was designed to give the payload the velocity and heading it needed to reach the vicinity of the moon in 2.6 days. At that time a rocket in the payload would be fired to alter the direction of travel of the payload and kick it into an orbit around the moon. It was to be no stunt; the payload would collect valuable scientific data needed to plan longer interplanetary shots and to prepare for the day when man himself would make the trip.

The problem of getting to the moon is complex. The earth spins on its axis once every twenty-four hours. This means that Cape Canaveral is moving to the east at about one thousand miles an hour due to earth rotation. At the same time the moon is revolving around the earth at a rate of about once every 27.3 days. Its distance from the earth's surface averages about 238,-000 miles, and its speed in orbit is about 2,300 miles an hour. The plane of the moon's rotation around the earth does not coincide with the earth's equatorial plane, these planes being displaced by about 18.5 degrees in 1958. As the moon goes around the earth, it climbs in the plane of its own orbit 18.5 degrees above the earth's equatorial plane, then crosses through the earth's equatorial plane and goes 18.5 degrees below it. This circuit is completed in a lunar month. The best shot at the moon would come when the launching point and the center of the earth lay in the plane of the moon's orbit. Cape Canaveral, at a latitude of 28 degrees above the equator, never lies in the plane of the moon's rotation; but at maximum declination, the angles are sufficiently close. Once the probe is launched in the plane of the moon's rotation or close to it, half the aiming problems are over. The worries about too high or too low are minimized. The main concern is about reaching the moon's orbit too early or too late. The moon reaches its maximum declination only once a month; this is why we were severely limited in the number of days that we could fire each month.

62

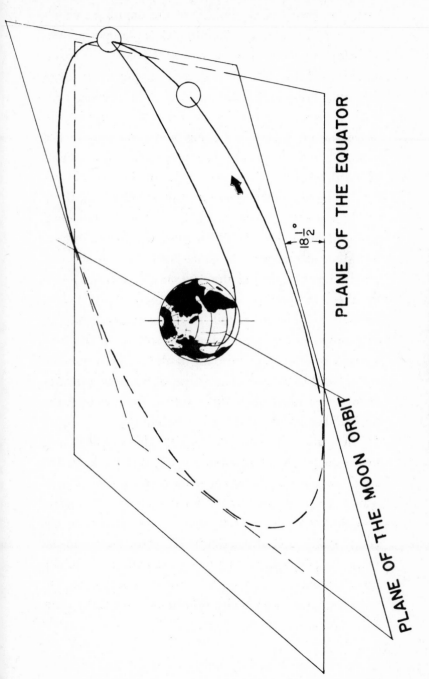

$18\frac{1}{2}°$

PLANE OF THE EQUATOR

PLANE OF THE MOON ORBIT

Typical Lunar Trajectory (Artist's Sketch)

Having thus chosen the day of the month on which to fire, the problem remained to pick the proper minute of the day for firing. The rotation of the earth, the speed of our payload, and the distance to the moon fixed the time. We wanted the payload to be moving relatively slowly when it came closest to the moon to improve the chances of its going into orbit around the moon when the payload rocket was fired. After burnout of the third stage, the speed of the payload would decrease because of the gravitational pull of the earth. It would reach its slowest speed at a distance about nine-tenths of the way to the moon when the moon's gravity would accelerate it again. Since we knew the effect of gravity on the speed of the payload, the time required for the trip and the velocity required at third-stage burnout could be computed. The velocity would have to be pointed in the proper direction so that in the time allotted for the trip, the path of the payload and the moon would intersect. The shape of the power-on trajectory and the launch time were chosen to give the payload the proper directional heading.

Perhaps another way to visualize this problem is to picture a jalopy going around a big dirt track. In the center of the track is a man on a merry-go-round who wants to throw a baseball to hit the jalopy. The merry-go-round is rotating pretty fast in comparison to the jalopy going around its circuit. We know where on the track the jalopy should be when the ball hits it (analogous to the day of the month). If the man throws the ball with the same speed and on the same path every time,

64

there is only one angular position on the merry-go-round from which he can throw the ball and hit the jalopy. That point is analogous to the optimum time for launch.

If all these calculations were right, and the missile's performance was within the expected limits, a launching at the optimum time gave odds of seventy chances out of one hundred of orbiting the moon. One minute later, it would have sixty-nine chances; thirty minutes later, thirty chances.

The planned flight was complex and intricate and contained a score of series events which had to occur in proper sequence and at the proper time to permit the payload to go on its way. The first stage would blast off from Pad 17-A. The second stage, fueled and armed, would wait for the signal from the first stage that indicated that its energy was exhausted. When the signal came through, the stages would separate and the second-stage Aerojet-General engine would start. Soon afterward the payload fairing would separate. The second stage had spin rockets aboard designed to impart a spin to the vehicle just before the third-stage separation. This spin would help stabilize the payload in its flight through space. The third stage would ignite after the second stage dropped off, and it would boost the payload to the required velocity. At third-stage burnout, the payload would separate and continue spinning into space. All these actions were like ladder steps—you couldn't get to the next rung until you passed the previous one.

65

The target, the moon, has been the object of study for generations, but what we know of it—which is little—has been learned by observation. We have not seen the other side of the moon, and one of the important functions of the payload would have been to get a "picture" of the far side of the moon with the televisionlike scanning device. The moon rotates on its axis once a month, generally keeping the same side toward the earth. We are able to see 41 per cent of the moon's surface at all times, another 41 per cent is never visible, and the remaining 18 per cent is alternately visible and invisible.

The diameter of the moon is 2,160 miles, or slightly more than one-fourth the size of the earth. The moon's force of gravity is one-sixth that of earth, so that an object weighing six pounds on earth would weigh but a pound on the moon. The moon's mass has been computed as 1/81.3 that of earth. The moon is alternately hotter and colder than earth because of its extremely tenuous (or completely absent) atmosphere; it is dotted with a dozen large mountain ranges as high as the Rockies; and more than thirty thousand craters can be seen on the side of the moon facing the earth.

This much and little more does man know of the moon. But now man is ready to attempt a probe into outer space in the vicinity of the mysterious moon. He is ready because he is backed up with 300 years of scientific and mathematical calculations and 15 years of intensive rocket research and development. For the first time he has the hardware.

This is what we knew from trajectory studies run by Space Technology Laboratories and Douglas. But these were only facts and figures on paper. The hardware would soon be on the pad.

We were still a long way from a lunar orbit.

# CHAPTER 6

The heartbeat of a countdown is ticked off in a drab, turtle-backed, heavily reinforced concrete building known as the blockhouse, built to withstand the impact of a crashing missile. And it can be a heaven, on the good days, and a hall of horrors, a living hell, on the others.

Here we toil the long hours before the missile leaves the ground. Here more than fifty of us watch the internal movements and variations of the missile by use of monitors which act like stethoscopes—their responses recorded in lights or charts or sound. We have no view of the missile after the T-35 counting begins except through a periscope and on small television monitors. Outside, the launching pad is a battlefield, and we are the field headquarters behind the lines in our shelter.

Our blockhouse at Cape Canaveral was located 600 feet to the rear of Pad 17-A, facing east; the pad was

Elevation view, south side of Blockhouse 17.

to the northeast. The single-story blockhouse, designed to be a strictly functional housing for firing, recording, and monitoring gear, was a structure to make even the poorest architect red with embarrassment, for it was dingy, cramped, and always cold. It was a Model A among blockhouses, and our people knew it. The Martin Co. took pride in its large Titan blockhouse, the one we called a split-level home. Convair was proud of its Atlas blockhouse, which had a glass-enclosed observation booth for visitors. Visitors—and there was always high-level personnel around during countdowns—to the Douglas blockhouse were shoved to one side, and they sat jammed together at a small table. We shared, we thought, a proud heritage with Douglas, for we considered the firm among the pioneers in aviation and rocketry, but we had no pride in this blockhouse which was supplied to us. Someone suggested turning the blueprints of it over to the Russians. If anything could slow down their missile pace, working in similar quarters was certainly one way. But we got the job done anyway. We were in this blockhouse because its plans were available early in the program and we needed a blockhouse in a hurry.

Physically, the blockhouse was as singularly unimpressive inside as out. The floor was finished in black asphalt tile and usually tracked with sandy footprints. We started using the blockhouse so soon after it was built that the tile floor had not been completed—but we needed no floor to get a missile off the ground. The ceiling was a mass of cable trays carrying wires to our consoles, to the pad outside and to Central Control, located three miles behind us. The base of the walls was lined with trenches carrying still more cables. Overhead hung office-type chandeliers, and battery-powered lamps hung clamped to the walls—just in case. This was the nerve center of our operation. Every internal missile function was recorded on consoles, or operating positions—machines painted gray, which were a mass of lights, knobs, buttons, gauges and dials. Operators sat before these consoles and commanded or monitored missile operation by pushing buttons to start some sequences, watching lights to see that others were going on or checking gauges to see that engine and propellant-system pressures were high enough or that the control system was swinging the engine properly.

There were three main rooms in the front of the blockhouse. The front room was wedge-shaped and contained the firing consoles. The consoles were lined up on the two sloping faces of the wedge. The Project Command console was in the apex of the wedge and was manned by the Test Conductor, Test Director, and Test Controller. Running part of the way up the middle of this room was a wall which split it roughly in half. We resented this wall since it impersonally split our front-room operation.

To the rear of the front room was the middle room, a rectangular room which contained our instrumentation distribution system and recorders.

The third room was actually two rooms, one housing the air-conditioning (the best in the world if you wanted

Blockhouse 17, south side of control room, looking west.

to freeze in sunny Florida), and the other had the Aero-jet-General consoles, Space Technology Laboratories consoles, our weights consoles, and timing and sequence equipment.

The back of the blockhouse was not built to be occupied during firings. There were three rooms in this relatively unprotected flank of the blockhouse—the men's rest room, an office for engineers stationed on the pad, and the lead technician's office.

The lead technician's office—he was responsible for keeping the blockhouse equipment in working condition—was dubbed Hernando's Hideaway. I'm glad Queen Fredericka of Greece didn't go into this office when she toured the Douglas blockhouse on a visit to the Cape, for the room was decorated with nude photographs from magazines. The Queen did, however, see one unscheduled art exhibit. Someone had pasted a nude on the face of a burned-out cathode-ray tube, and as she passed it her daughter nudged Her Majesty. The Queen was heard to say, "Oh, Marilyn Monroe."

The men's room also had a name. It was called the "House of Pogo." Some wag put the sign up on the door. It was named for Dick Pugeau of Douglas who is known simply as Pogo and is a good-natured engineer, the butt of many jokes. On the door there was a Vip cartoon from *True* magazine showing a soldier with his arms spread wide to keep a group of other soldiers from entering a latrine—a latrine he obviously had been captain of and which was sparkling clean. "Over my dead body," he was saying.

The blockhouse was our home away from home. I sometimes felt as if I had spent a lifetime in the blockhouse. There were hours of deep and lingering boredom, and some of bright and thrilling excitement; there were hours when I wished I were someplace else, and other hours when I was glad I was there. It was a home, we used to say. Sometimes a home for the aged, sometimes a joyous nursery. Perhaps some day archaeologists will be digging in the crust over Cape Canaveral and will come across that structure. What kind of man could have lived in such a building? will be their puzzled question.

What kind of man, indeed.

Elevation view, east side of Blockhouse 17.

# CHAPTER 7

The running of a countdown is a team effort. The team drills and rehearses and operates together toward a common goal—the launching. On some days the team is clicking, it can't make a mistake; on other days there are fumbles.

The job of the Test Conductor is to organize the work of the countdown into manageable units, into blocks of related jobs, so that the team can handle them with speed, safety, and efficiency. These blocks are called "tasks," and the senior engineer charged with accomplishing each task is the task leader. Our task leaders were veteran missilemen, men who had been through it before with Thor and other missiles and knew the idiosyncrasies of their systems like a book. They didn't have to stop and think which was the right valve to turn—they knew. They lived with the hardware. On the day of a count they were the leaders, reporting to the Test

Conductor and charged with the responsibility of getting the job done.

There was Ed Parker, Engine Control, the task leader for our engine checks on the first stage. In the terminal count Ed, standing behind the engine monitor consoles, raised his thumb to show me the engine was ready. Ed is only twenty-nine years old, physically slight and unassuming, but behind him are years of Nike missile engine work and experience on the Thor. Ed disappeared for a couple of days after a particularly good Thor shoot. Nobody could find him. When he finally showed up, he had some wonderful stories to tell about night life in Havana. We still rib him about the trip.

There was Ken Young, a big, handsome boy, our Missile Control. He was the task leader for the first-stage electrical checks. In the terminal count Ken indicated that the missile's electrical systems were ready with his upturned thumb. At the field station Ken was in charge of the equipment group. His knowledge of missile systems, combined with his innate ability to lead men, enabled him to mold his group into a tightly knit organization with tremendous *esprit de corps*. Every Friday night the group met down at the River's Edge Restaurant and Bar for a TGIF (Thank God it's Friday) party. Bill Button took over as equipment group leader when Ken was called back to Santa Monica for a promotion. Bill, short and stocky, once lost a box of cigars to me. He was standing next to me in a particularly rough Thor countdown. We had been through the terminal count several times, and each time, just before reaching zero, something insignificant stopped us from firing. Just as we were about to try it again, Bill turned to me and said, "By God, if we make it through this time, I'll buy you a box of cigars." We made it.

Joe Broadbent and Hal Eaton were our "men with the golden fingers." Joe manned the launch control console and pushed the firing button at zero time on the first lunar probe, Hal on the last two. There is one instant in a countdown when Launch Control and I function as a single person. As the Timer drones, ". . . three, two . . ." Launch Control turns to me and we exchange a single glance. If my thumb is up, we go.

Earle Wollam was my understudy, and as such he did a lion's share of the dog work, and there is a lot of dog work in preparing for and executing a countdown. Earle is the kind of person to whom you can give an assignment and never hear from until he has accomplished it, neatly and with dispatch. He had a big part in working out the new countdown concept for the lunar probes. During many of the long hours Earle handled the count, and he did it with the firm voice of authority.

There was Dick Morrison of Space Technology Laboratories. He was Able director, the over-all authority on the preparation and readiness of the Able components— the components above the first stage. Dick was tall and a baggy-tweeds-type of college professor. He was extremely well liked and respected. He was on sabbatical leave from the University of Michigan and took the job to "get the feel" of industry. We were sorry to see him go back to school.

These people, and many more like them, turned the blue loose-leaf book, labeled *Thor Able-I Countdown,* into physical action and reality.

Under the task leaders were the technicians and mechanics of Douglas, Aerojet and Space Technology Laboratories. These people did the work. If the task leaders were the backfield of the team, the mechanics were the line. The center was the Stand Talker, Jim Kershaw. Jim's job was to move his people where they would be needed, to co-ordinate the shop's activities on the launcher, and to anticipate the man-power needs of the task leaders. Jim was a husky man, an ex-stock car driver. He knew his men; he knew the countdown. He was the first-stage crew chief.

The inspectors are a group apart. They are not integrated into any task as such, yet they must certify to the Test Conductor that the missile is ready to be fired. They watch each task. They check off their "inspection items" to make sure that critical safety operations are accomplished. When a door or box on the missile is closed for the last time, an inspector seals it with his stamp after making certain that the work has been done properly. These stamps are inspected to make sure the missile stays "finaled." When safety blocks or pins are removed, the inspector checks them off. These are turned over to the Test Conductor before the terminal count.

There is another backfield. In this line-up, the Test Conductor is the quarterback of the team and Project Command is his backfield. Project Command is composed of the Douglas Test Conductor, the Space Technology Laboratories Test Director, and the Air Force Ballistic Missile Division Test Controller. On matters involving deviations in test objectives or that possibly compromise the missile's ability to perform its mission, Project Command jointly formulates the decision. Project Command is the ultimate authority in a countdown —there is no higher appeal. The fact that it is located in the blockhouse and has authority commensurate with its responsibility means that there are no long-distance phone calls to review decisions before they are final, no remote controlling of the operation. Other projects have been hampered by long-distance direction.

Miles (Mike) Ross serves as Test Director in Project Command. He is tall, likable, and fun-loving. He is also an experienced missileman, having spent a number of years with Convair in missile flight testing at Inyokern, California. Mike loves long, expensive cigars and is constantly (but good-naturedly) bemoaning the fact that when we bum a cigar from him we get a good one; when he bums one from us he gets a dud. "When are you guys going to get a raise so that you can afford better cigars for me to steal?" he says.

Captain (now Major) M. E. Griffith—nobody knows what M. E. stands for, we call him Brandy—served as Test Controller. He remained in contact with the Superintendent of Range Operations during our terminal count. His thumbs-up meant that our systems were "go" and we had a "clear to launch" from the range.

Two other Air Force Ballistic Missile Division officers

83

remained in the blockhouse with us. One was Lieutenant Colonel Tom Morgan, the Thor project officer for the Air Force. Tom is an easygoing, savvy guy who will probably wind up a general one day. He has six (or is it seven) children. With all that progeny he had to be easygoing. Major Hal Myers, the Thor airframe officer under Morgan, stayed at the Project Command console with us, available for quick consultation in last-second decisions.

This was our backfield: Gordon, the Test Conductor; Ross, of Space Technology Laboratories; Griffith, Morgan, and Myers, of Ballistic Missile Division, Air Force. We stood at the Project Command console. With us was our Timer, measuring off the yardage needed for a touchdown, so to speak. The Timer announced the time before firing, first at half-hour intervals, then every five minutes, then, as time drew near, every thirty seconds. Finally, in the last fifteen seconds, he called out each second.

Morgan, as a consultant, sat nearby with our Talker, whose job it was to read out from the countdown document the steps to be performed, going down the list of flight-ready items to be accomplished in the last 35 minutes. Each item read over the intercom is an instruction to a console operator. The Talker waits until he hears that the action required has been completed by the console operator before reading the next item. He is an important member of the team. He can't stutter.

We call the hierarchy, the high-level planners of our project, "elder philosophers." The most realistic of our

84

philosophers was Bob Johnson, chief engineer for missiles and space systems of Douglas Aircraft. Bob says, "You've got to fly them to find out what you don't know." Bob is an ex-Navy lieutenant and came up through the ranks of the missiles engineering department.

George Butler of Douglas was the Thor Special Projects Engineer at the Santa Monica plant. Much of the Douglas part of the planning and design was co-ordinated by Butler. Young, dynamic and energetic, he also was an experienced missileman.

Dr. A. K. (Dolph) Thiel of Space Technology Laboratories was one of the mainstays of the Thor projects. Dolph was Program Director for Thor at Space Technology Laboratories and Mike Ross's boss. He came over with Dr. Wernher von Braun's team after World War II and worked at the Army Ballistic Missile Agency at Huntsville, Alabama, with the German team before going out into industry. In his position as Program Director, Dolph was largely responsible for his firm's policy on Thor. He is extremely strong-willed and very likable, but in the blockhouse he was a worrier. If everything was going smoothly, Dolph worried. With problems, he was even more worried.

Bill Duval was our field-station manager. Bill was a forceful man and brought with him to Canaveral the experience he gained in organizing and managing the Douglas field station at White Sands Proving Grounds. Bill Stitt, his technical assistant, usually stayed in the blockhouse during the countdowns. The

85

two Bills put our ground installations together and got the ball rolling when Douglas first came to the East Coast. Stitt was our first launch-area engineer, and his phenomenal memory of what went into Complex 17-A pulled us out of more than one tight scrape. It was a standing joke that as soon as the blockhouse doors closed at T-35 minutes, Stitt would have to go to the head. We came to look on his trips as good-luck omens.

At the top of these elder philosophers were the corporate heads, the organizers, the men who had enough faith in the team and the hardware to shoot the moon: Donald Douglas and Donald Douglas, Jr.; Dr. Louis Dunn and Dr. Rube Mettler, of Space Technology Laboratories; Major General Schriever; Dr. T. K. Glennan, of the National Aeronautics and Space Administration; Roy Johnson, of the Advanced Research Projects Agency; and Defense Department Secretary McElroy.

Who can list the whole team? It would be impossible. The Rocketdyne engineers on the hill at Santa Susana, California, testing Thor engines, were a part of the team. The mathematical analysts computing trajectories on the West Coast were part of the team. The Range Safety Officer, the tracking station operators, even the chow-wagon operator, were part of the team. We didn't even know them all, but we did know they would be watching and waiting with the rest of the world, and we were going to do our damnedest for them.

# CHAPTER 8

The team had been chosen. The first stage was on the launching pad. Workers prepared the other stages in Canaveral's hangars. It was time now for final detailed planning.

We co-ordinated our planning in a small conference room upstairs in Hangar L in the industrial area of Cape Canaveral. Many different large and powerful corporations were involved in Project Able-I, but we had to meet on common ground and we had to cut through intercompany red tape. In the Thor program we had established the Flight Test Working Group—FTWG—to manage the program in the field. Each associate contractor had one representative on the committee who had the authority to "speak for his company." In this way we could decide last-minute problems without waiting for feedback from our home plants. The Flight Test Working Group structure had worked well in the

Able program, and it was carried through into the program of Project Able-I.

We were meeting one day to confirm our planned activities prior to firing the first probe. It was July 28, 1958, and the firing was three weeks away. Mike Ross presided over the meeting. Dick Morrison and his top aide, Bob Bennett, a brilliant young Ph.D., represented the second-, third- and payload-stage hardware people. Colonel Tom Morgan was there for the Air Force's Ballistic Missile Division. I represented Douglas Aircraft.

Here is the plan we had: for the rest of the week we would continue checking the Thor which was already erected on 17-A. The hangar checks would continue on the second, third, and payload stages. Then, early in the week of August 4, we would mate the second and a dummy third stage to the Thor. We didn't want to use the actual third stage since it was loaded with solid propellants and ready to go. After the mating we would conduct compatibility checks to make sure the stages, mated for the first time, worked properly together. On August 8 we would conduct a mock countdown. This would be our first operational check of our still-theoretical new format. This mock countdown was to be a simulation of all countdown tasks. If necessary, we would spend Saturday, the 9th, and Sunday, the 10th, repeating the rehearsal. On the 11th a world-wide communications check was to be conducted to make sure all tracking stations and Cape Canaveral were linked properly to the Data Reduction Center at Inglewood, California. As of the day of the meeting, the communication links were not yet completed. On Wednesday, the 13th, we would go into our formalized precountdown checkouts of the missile and facilities. The 14th would be T-2 day, and the 15th T-1 day. At 5 P.M. that day, the 15th, we would have our final pre-count review. Everything had to be complete by that time. The countdown would begin on the 16th, and the actual firing would take place on the 17th if everything went right.

We broke up, eager to go.

# CHAPTER 9

The hour of launch was rushing up on us. It was days away—hectic days away—but each day seemed to have fewer and fewer hours. Even the nights became tense. Normally, I am a good and sound sleeper, but I rolled and tossed in those last few nights. Seldom do I hear the cries of the children in the night when they meet some grizzly bear in their dreams, but I heard them much those nights in our home in Titusville.

It was hard to relax and get on a fairly even keel before bedtime, so I resorted to an old diversion, ham radio. I sat before the set in our dining area and called ham friends in all parts of the country and chatted—ham talk with little meaning but with considerable entertainment value. Little did they know that they were helping Ted Gordon—W4TEC—calm his jittery nerves.

Whenever I stopped to think of the job ahead and

Missile 127 on launching pad 17A with gantry in place.

what we were trying to do, I was struck with the magnitude of the thing. I had helped in missile preparation before, and the summer had been active with tough, tense countdowns on the Able re-entry shoots. But the possibilities and the meaning of the impending shots were staggering. Every now and then I looked at the missile being mated on the pad and said to myself, "This thing is aimed at the moon. This missile is going to be man's first attempt to shoot toward the moon."

This was a large missile on the launch pad. I had worked on the sleek Nikes at White Sands, and I remember the impression of bigness I had when I first saw the Thor. I remember that I was amazed that a man could lie across the engine compartment without his head or toes touching the sides. Now, stacked on top of our 62-foot Thor, would be another 26 feet of stages!

Security won't let me say how many launchings I have taken part in, but I can say that every one supplied a thrill. There is no exhilaration quite like that of seeing a missile leave the pad on a tower of flame and disappear in the sky. Nor is there any depression quite like the vast and deep one following the sight of failure or explosion of this instrument on which you have toiled so hard.

The missile is not feminine like a ship or aircraft, and it is seldom spoken of in endearing terms. It is usually simply "it," and I doubt if missilemen feel a warm kinship to a missile, a love for the instrument such as men at sea feel for a ship. Some day, when men fly into space, their missile ships will be "she's" again. But as

93

yet, missiles aren't quite humanized. They are still products of man, not companions. The missile is more often than not simply a "bastard"—yet there is a sincere and strong feeling of devotion to it, not because of its beauty (though the Thor is a beautiful thing), but more because it carries the hopes and dreams and labor of thousands of men and women, civilian and military, every time it tries to lift itself from the launching pad. And, as Jack Bromberg used to impress upon us, it carried a hope of peace for the world, for we never could forget that here was basically a ballistic missile designed for defense of the free world. But now we were at work on a lunar probe, a test with scientific goals. We could put away thoughts of a warhead in the nose cone.

The first probe was, of course, scheduled for August 17 at 7:14 A.M., Eastern Standard Time. The complete missile was mated on Complex 17-A early in the week of August 4. After this mating we checked all systems of the missile, and, when this was finished to our satisfaction, we felt we had achieved success in the first big step toward the final qualification for flight.

The Thor booster was a relatively simple vehicle to check out now, compared to the standard Thor. Instrumentation was reduced because of weight requirements and the number of tracking aids, beacons, and other items to be checked was fewer than normal. The second stage had only simple telemetry on board and its check-out was straightforward. The crew had checked out the first two stages before, because they were used to much the same configuration in the Thor-Able shoots.

94

Missile 127 erect in launch position during a mock firing at a countdown rehearsal. The nine-story gantry has been pulled back.

The first three stages were mated now (the third stage was a dummy stage, the propellant was inert), and all we had left to mate was the fourth, or payload, stage. It had been assembled on the West Coast and was being checked for the last time. Now we were ready to test our new countdown format, and on August 8 we conducted a mock countdown.

The practice countdown was almost as nerve-tingling as the real thing, for up to this point the only thing we had was a carefully prepared piece of paper. The mock countdown ran through the tasks in minute detail, just as if we were going to fire. We went through simulated propellant loading, engine checks and destruct tests. We checked electrical systems, ordnance tasks—everything. It took us almost as much time as a real countdown. The tower was moved back and we approached a simulated terminal count.

Then we received an ominous weather report: a prediction of thunderstorms with possible lightning. This didn't make us feel at all easy or comfortable. During the mock countdown we did not load the missile with propellants, so there was no danger of an explosion if lightning struck the missile, but it could short-circuit or knock out the electrical systems, and that could delay us for a long while. Or lightning could do serious structural damage. Lightning was always a touchy thing to deal with. We kept our fingers crossed.

The weather cleared and we were in our terminal count. "Lift-off" was accomplished after a minute hold by Range Safety, and we considered the test a success.

However, we still did not have complete assurance even after this test that we could fire at a particular time. Personnel performance in a mock countdown can be totally different from the real thing. However, we did gain some degree of confidence from the countdown. We felt that our new countdown concept was good.

But we were not certain. We still had to wait for the final test, a moon shot.

On Monday, August 11, a world-wide communications check was conducted and all went well. This was one of our last big hurdles, and we were elated to receive the good report.

Preparations had been made to track the missile in flight and to receive telemetry data from the missile on its journey through space. The idea was to establish enough ground stations to keep the missile "in view" throughout its projected flight. These stations had to be set up with a telephone-teletype network connecting each one of them with the Center for trajectory analysis and data reduction in California.

Our plan was to have stations widely dispersed, so General Schriever and his staff set out to find the right and practicable points. Five stations were set up. Three of them had already been made operational before the program began. The three were Patrick Air Force Base, Westford, Massachusetts, and Manchester, England. The British offered the use of their big radio telescope, the largest in the world, and we were delighted to have their co-operation and wonderful facilities. They then

The ground radio-telescope near Manchester, England. The generator room is at the right.

gave us another big break when they made available a station in Singapore.

General Schriever had been looking for a site in the Philippines, but his technicians reported that there was such a high level of electromagnetic noise in the area that a station in the islands was impractical. This came as a surprise, for the Air Force had expected no noise level of this type in the sector. Then they got an explanation, an eyebrow-lifting one: Filipinos were constantly talking back and forth from village to village on small transmitters salvaged from World War II. The site in Singapore would be just as good, and would not have the noise drawback.

Ideally, the fifth site we wanted was in the Hawaiian Islands. Fortunately, Schriever's men found a location there. Its importance depended on the island's being beneath the intercept point of the payload and the moon—if our trajectory was properly executed. A trailer was also set up on the beach at Hilo in which Henry Samulon, a Polish-born electronics engineer, would wait for the signal to fire the retro rocket in the payload stage and kick the payload into orbit around the moon.

Equipping the sites was a gigantic job, a task tackled in April and completed in August just in time for the world-wide communications check. This meant transporting thousands of tons of antennae and electronics gear from Boston and Los Angeles to the overseas sites, setting that equipment up and getting it quickly into operational condition. The Air Force did the job—and each station was soon linked to the California Data Reduction Center. All this was a tremendous task. In years to come all this will be considered one of the outstanding communication feats of our time.

On August 12 and 13 we went through the final requalification of all our systems to make certain the missile was ready to go into final countdown checks. On August 14, 1958, we executed the checks scheduled for T-2 day.

Tension was building now like a head of steam. It was intensified by the great amount of publicity our project received. There wasn't a room to be had along the Florida coast for miles around. Newsmen from all over the world had flocked to the Canaveral area to see the first lunar probe. Air Force public-relations officers had briefed the newsmen. The newsmen were on "standby" at the Starlite, Vanguard, and Missile motels, awaiting word to report to Patrick for transportation to the Cape for the missile shoot. Throughout the whole area the lunar probe was the foremost topic of conversation wherever you went. Lunar probes were about as secret now as a woman's conversation in a beauty parlor. No one knew T-time, but everyone seemed to know that within 48 hours something important would happen.

To top it all off, Hurricane Cleo was reportedly headed for the Florida coast. It was anybody's guess where Cleo would hit the coast, but we felt certain that our luck would be so bad that Cleo would hit near us.

I don't think I have ever felt more apprehensive. Big wheels from Washington and top brass from Douglas were arriving at the Cape. The whole world was looking over our shoulders as we got down to the last hours. No longer were we in a security-tight project. Our business was everybody's business.

Missile 127 was extremely "clean" from the beginning. This was a good thing, and it helped build our confidence. We held our T-1 day meeting at 5 P.M. on the 15th, and the meeting ended on a note of optimism. I stood before the group and ran down a list of things to be checked. Everyone gave me good reports.

We were ready now to go into the "finaling" procedure—checks by Douglas inspection and manufacturing departments. This was our last look around the whole missile itself—the engine section and guidance sections —to make sure all the plugs were in and safely wired. The inspectors had to certify that Missile 127 was ready for flight—mechanically and electrically.

After the meeting on T-1 day, I left the Cape at 6:30 P.M. and drove to Titusville. My thought, as I drove home that night, was that when I came over that road again I would be coming back to shoot the moon. I wondered how I would feel the next time I headed home— joyful and satisfied or infinitely dejected?

This Thor program had had its share of successes and failures. Other shoots had been like that, too. There is a nice, warm feeling if things go well, and when things go badly a nagging question, "Was it something I did?" But tomorrow's shoot was likely to be the biggest shoot of my career, or of anyone's career, and I knew we could not tolerate failure.

That night a newspaperman from North Carolina

found me at home. He had come to talk with me on the eve of the big shoot, to write a human-interest story on the "first man to shoot the moon" and that man's reactions. The man from North Carolina wanted to know how I felt, what was going on in my mind, and my over-all reaction.

He kept prodding me. "How do you feel?" he asked. "What are you thinking?" I felt very inadequate. Here I was calmly sitting in my living room, the hi-fi speaker blaring out Louis Armstrong recordings, the kids tucked in bed, Annie talking about buying a new living-room rug. In a few hours I would begin the terminal countdown for the moon.

My mind went back to the mock countdown the week before, the day we rolled the tower away from the missile. I stood then on the launching pad and looked up at the missile. This is simply fabulous, I had said to myself.

The whole past week—from the mock countdown to this night before the shoot—had been a little unreal. I tried to do things that would distract me. I went to Cocoa one day and bought a new Ella Fitzgerald album; I tried to balance the bankbook, a feat almost impossible in my household; I drove the Healey across the flat Florida wastes late at night to blow the cobwebs out of my mind.

I was a bit unnerved, I admit. A lot could go wrong. You have to make quick decisions. The first time I was Test Conductor on the Thor I was nervous, but soon we got to working as a team. Now the old nervousness was back again.

Missilemen are a strange breed, and this was the strangest night of all for all of us. Our hopes and dreams are built on a button. If everything goes well we have a highball and have a good time. If things don't go well we just have a highball.

I tried not to be dramatic about it. I wasn't bringing my tension and troubles home with me. I was still hungry at mealtimes. I still had bills to pay, children to discipline, a wife to keep happy. But I was aware, at the same time, of the import of this thing. I knew that if I had been asked, just ten years before, when I was an eighteen-year-old student at Louisiana State University, what I would like to do some day, this would have been it. Few have been so lucky. Yet I felt the tremendous weight on my shoulders as I talked with the reporter. I felt I had the hopes of thousands resting on my decisions.

It was just tremendous, by God, just tremendous.

# CHAPTER 10

Instead of getting up at dawn the next day and heading straight for the Cape, I stayed around the house in Titusville and tried to relax. I was awake early, following my usual habit, but tried to stay in bed a few minutes longer. I lay there and listened to the noises around me—the staccato tapping of a workman's hammer on the house being built down the road, the rattling of pots and pans in the kitchen and the laughter of children playing outside very early in the heat of the August morning.

But there was no real relaxation. Finally I headed for the Cape and got to work at 10 A.M., going directly to my office in the hangar. Time was dragging now. This was the awful, dull, listless period, a few hours before tasks were to begin. There was nothing to do but to sit and wait. At my desk I tried to clear away some paper work. That was no use, my mind wasn't on it.

At 1:30 P.M., August 16, the T-time was 765 min-

Fueling the second stage of a space probe vehicle.
Protective suits are worn because of corrosive fuels.

utes away, apart from the recognized no-work periods. It was still a long while before launch time. Fueling tasks had started and I went to the blockhouse from the hangar. This was what we called Able fueling, fueling of the second stage, and it was spectacular to watch. The men who fuel wear acid protection suits and look like the space fiction artists' conceptions of men from Mars—or from the moon. The large propellant storage tanks are delivered to us by Pan American, are hoisted up the service tower, and the second stage is fed from them. We had no difficulty except that there was some concern over the weight console monitor's giving accurate readings of the total missile weight, but this wasn't an important problem. The task was completed ahead of schedule, and at 6 P.M. we had a no-work period for two hours.

There was nothing here, not even in a countdown for a moon shoot, to intrigue the Hollywood script writer. It had been a long day, and once we stopped our tasks the weight of fatigue crashed down upon us. We sat around with our feet propped on desks and talked or dozed. The minute hands on the clocks around us moved ever so slowly.

Often, to break the monotony, we used to get a bite to eat from the Pan Am food truck when it made stops irregularly at the rear of the blockhouse. The large trucks had counters from which attendants served a few hot things—hot dogs, coffee. A truck like this was known rather unaffectionately as the "garbage scow" or "roach coach." The name never endeared us to the operators. Once during a slack afternoon, Ken Young yelled out, "Garbage wagon coming," and we jumped up and ran for the exit, hoping to get in front of the inevitable line for a sandwich. Lumbering through the gate was a garbage truck, a real one.

After Able fueling, the built-in no-work period was scheduled to be released at 8:05 P.M., when time would be T-490 minutes. To save extra time for later no-work periods, we released engine checks at 7:45 P.M., about 20 minutes early. I was glad when we swung back in operation. The two hours had been long and boring. The problems in engine checks were minor and electrical checks were released in parallel with the remaining engine checks at 8:55 P.M. We were still slightly ahead of schedule.

Everything was going fairly well. It was chilly as the men climbed about the lighted service tower at their tasks. They looked like construction workers building a skyscraper, but there were no loud noises, only the occasional barking of the public address system. To break away from the oppressive confinement in the blockhouse, I would go outside and walk down the road to the pad and walk about the missile. It looked light blue as it rested in the service tower. Off to the left I saw the blinking of the Canaveral lighthouse and to the south I could see the lights of Cocoa Beach. The night was calm and black, the sky dotted with stars and the silence was punctuated by the occasional cry of a crane or the squawking of a sea gull.

We had a few headaches. There was a problem in

110

our pneumatic console, a gadget which supplies gas pressure from the ground to the first stage. A wire, we found, had broken, and we repaired it quickly. During our electrical systems checks, Able telemetry—the telemetry for the upper stages—reported "no-go," but all other systems reported "go." We resolved this problem shortly when we found a connector that had not been inserted properly. Out of sequence, we turned the telemetry on as a special test with the range. We wanted to know if they could receive it. They reported at 11:35 P.M. that they could see the second-stage telemetry O.K. A sigh of relief again.

Next we ran our destruct tests at 12:30 A.M. Suddenly I realized that it was now August 17. What had happened to August 16? That earlier day had alternately been a week long and minutes long. The destruct tests were the last chance the Range Safety Officer had to be sure he could destroy a missile deviating from the predicted path. The tests were run. Again everything was all right.

At 2 A.M. we got another two-hour no-work period. Through all these hours in the blockhouse I wore a headset which tied me to a plug-jack. I had to pull a coil of wire with me wherever I went. Everyone was constantly stepping over wires. The set made my head feel as though it were being pinched in. I was just plain uncomfortable, and I didn't look forward to another two hours of sitting around. I took off the set, went to the shop building and got a cup of bean soup with Jack Bromberg. The soup came from a machine, and that machine had made us great bean-soup drinkers by this time.

Our countdown had been extremely clean to this point. We were still ahead of schedule. If it keeps up this way, I thought, I may set a record for bean-soup consumption. Everyone's fatigue was great—we had been going some 14 hours. I felt very sleepy as soon as I gave up and slumped into a chair.

Our next task after this no-work period was LOXing, or putting the liquid oxygen in the first stage of the missile. We were scheduled to release the no-work period at 4 A.M. (T-135 minutes). However, we began the LOXing task at 3:40 A.M. The countdown was resumed at 4 A.M., with LOXing well under way.

Liquid oxygen is very cold—minus 297 degrees F. As the liquid oxygen reached the much warmer pipes, a high, screaming sound, which sends chills up your back, was heard over the area. That sound is part wail, screaming, screeching—one of the most frightening sounds in the world. Vapor from the LOX engulfed the entire base of the missile, a fluffy white cloud which hung onto the service tower like a big puff of smoke around a pipe-smoker's head. A small vapor vent near the middle of the missile's first stage was opened to allow vapor to escape and so prevent too much pressure from being built up. A stream of LOX vapor poured out of the vent. The LOX in the missile's belly now turns it very cold and the whole missile begins to take on a definite bluish look as the man-made frost begins to creep over it with the fueling. Missile 127 looked like an inverted icicle sitting there in the gray light of dawn

112

—dawn which was beginning to wash across the sky and push the dark clouds of night away from the pad on which we worked against time.

Next came regulator settings and the helium leak check—and we were ready for the dramatic moment, the time when we moved the tower away from the missile. At 5 A.M. we started moving the tower. This was one of the crucial segments of the countdown.

The service tower (or gantry) which surrounds the missile is a structure much like a painter's or builder's scaffolding. It is made in sections of various heights and each section has a platform of semicircular cutouts which are north and south of the missile. For instance, one level is at the elevation of the payload, another where the payload and third stage are joined, another where the first and second stages are mated. These platforms allow men to work on the outside of the missile. Once the platforms are raised, the entire tower, which weighs tons, is rolled back on its own wheels. The tower is moved by means of drive motors which pull it on railroad tracks. Since the tower is moved in a crucial part of the countdown—fuel and part of the LOX aboard and most tasks already performed—it is essential that the tower be moved on schedule and without delay. In the lunar probe countdown, where we were striving for a firing within a narrow tolerance, we could tolerate no delays.

Searchlights were now on, and the frosted missile was wrapped in the steely white glow of the lights. The signal was given for moving the tower. The grind of the motors began. The tower inched back.

113

Now a red light flashed on top of the blockhouse—a signal that firing was imminent, although we were two hours away from T-time. The missile rested on the pad, glowing in the searchlights, pointed skyward and no longer held by the gantry. A trail of vapor was still pouring from the LOX tank vent.

The countdown so far was on schedule. Two-thirds of the LOX was aboard. Missile 127 was fueled. It was 5:39 A.M. now, but we still had a no-work period. We had 60 minutes to wait. I kept my fingers crossed. All had gone well. We were ready for T-35 minutes.

The sun was coming up, signaling a clear, bright day. Outside the morning seemed to come to life. A breeze fanned across the Cape. The next hour would be eternity. I rearranged the papers on the Project Command table, I pulled at the coils of my uncomfortable headset, I lit another cigar. I went to the garbage scow again and got a cup of coffee.

The minutes ticked off as if the hands of the clock barely had the power to make it to the top of the face. My assistant, Earle Wollam, marked figures on a chalkboard. He kept a chart of the elapsed time, the T-times, the times of each task. "Can't you keep the minutes straight?" I kidded him. "You can't be right." It was a complicated job, but the times were correct. We just had to wait.

Finally the hands on the clock showed 6:39.

It was T-35 minutes. No more no-work periods, no more holds. I was no longer bored, no longer tired. Missile 127's terminal countdown had begun.

114

Space probe vehicle ready to go, immediately before final countdown.

# CHAPTER 11

We manned our stations for the terminal count. I was nervous. My mind kept going back over a thousand details, wondering if this had been checked properly, if our modifications would work, if everyone knew his job. This was a highly skilled, well-trained and experienced team—but one minute slip or misjudgment could mean the end of a glorious experiment.

We put on our shoot shirts just before T-35. These are white sports shirts with DOUGLAS in red letters across the back and under that in smaller, blue letters the title of our positions. We feel the shirts give us team spirit though we often kid about the college rah-rah. For good luck in countdowns I wear an old red sports shirt underneath. The doors were closed now, cigars—nearly all of us smoke them—were lit, and the Timer began calling out the minutes; the Talker followed with commands and then waited for the console operators to answer:

"T minus thirty-five minutes—*mark*."

"Check payload ready."

"Ready."

"Able ground power on."

"On."

"Able accelerometer heat on."

"On."

"Stand fog and deluge disable."

"Disable."

"Increase water pressure."

"Roger."

"Able missile power on."

"On."

"Start audio recorders."

"Started."

The countdown continued, the Timer reading the minutes from the clock on the wall in front of the Project Command console, the Talker rattling off the items listed in the countdown manual, the console operators carrying out the commands and giving the prearranged answer for each item. But at T-24 minutes we experienced some trouble.

"T minus twenty-four minutes . . . *mark*."

"Enable firex."

"Enable."

"Able accelerometer caged."

"Caged."

"Able accelerometer heat off."

"Off."

We started to get some questionable reports on the

118

payload telemetry. We wrestled with the question for nine minutes, going through tortuous mental gymnastics. This was critical. There wouldn't be any reason to shoot if payload telemetry didn't work. This was a scientific experiment and we were seeking scientific data from the instruments in the payload. The telemetry was our radio link between the payload package and the ground stations. At T-15 minutes, just 15 minutes before the lunar probe rocket was scheduled to fire, I called a hold. The telemetry was not indicating proper performance. Dick Morrison, Able control, was on my right in the front of the blockhouse. Some locally generated signal was making the payload telemetry appear inoperative. I called a quick consultation among Dick Morrison, Brandy Griffith, Mike Ross, and Hal Myers. Dick was talking to his electronics experts over the intercom. It was a hair-raising time, for we didn't know what to do.

I suddenly remembered that first talk with Jim Gunkel. Could we fire at a given time, a spread of 15 or 20 minutes? We thought we could, but now I was not at all certain. We had gone through two days of countdown procedure without much trouble—and now, in the short minutes before lift-off, this had to happen. We searched our souls.

I released the hold after four minutes. This was a tough decision, but we felt that we were right. Our opinion was that most probably the interference was due to some locally generated signal somewhere in the area—perhaps a microwave link that some television

119

people had set up. We weren't sure, we didn't know. We felt the chances were that this was the cause of the problem; the payload telemetry had checked out before and was working properly earlier in the count. If we were correct, the trouble would clear up when the missile passed beyond range of the local signal.

We decided it was worth a risk. We had enough invested in the countdown to that point to make it worthwhile to continue. This was our most anxious moment. I know we are right, I told myself, and I was confident, though anxious, when we resumed the counting. It was 7:03 A.M., we had lost four minutes, and the countdown went without a hitch to 7:18 A.M.

At T minus 30 seconds the last items were read by the Talker.

"Start tanks."

"Pressurized."

"Open vernier fuel vent."

"Open."

"Check arm."

"Armed."

Then the last seconds . . . "five, four, three. . . ."

Brandy Griffith heard from the Superintendent of Range Operations that everything was O.K. with them, and his thumb went up. The engine monitors saw that engine pressures were O.K., and the monitor behind the console lifted his thumb. Missile control was all right. My thumb is the sum of all the thumbs. It was up. Joe Broadbent looked at me. The clock on the wall stood at 7:18 A.M.

120

"Go, baby, go."

". . . Two, one, zero."

Joe saw my thumb and pressed the button on the launch-control console. The lights clicked off in sequence; the first lit, then the second, the third, the fourth. They were all on, the automatic start sequence had gone through the process of starting the main engine. The lights were glowing—and it was lift-off.

I called out, "Lift-off." Dick Morrison said the same thing so personnel on his intercom loop would know that their firing procedure (for the payload verniers) was next.

There was much shouting and cheering in the blockhouse, not so much because of the lift-off as because of our relief that we had perfected the countdown procedure. We had come within four minutes of earliest allowable launch time and this made us cry out with excitement.

For a missile length we could see the lift-off visually on the TV monitor. We could hear the low rumble in the blockhouse as the powerful Rocketdyne engines pushed Missile 127 up—a rumble that hits you fast in the belly and gradually fades away.

When the missile was out of the television picture we could tell through two sources that it was climbing. One was the telemetry monitor in the blockhouse to my right and the other was via the intercom from Central Control. At Central Control the Superintendent of Range Operations could see the Range Safety plotting boards. His plots showed the missile programming down the predicted path.

The SRO talked to Griffith over the intercom. "Clean lift-off, Brandy," he reported. I walked over to the telemetry console and watched the presentation there. We saw that the engine was working properly and that the missile was still under control.

But at 77 seconds we knew something was wrong.

# CHAPTER 12

I pulled off my shoot shirt, and one thought ran through my mind: "Did I do something that caused this?"

It looked as though the failure at 77 seconds of flight had been in the first stage, the Douglas Thor, and this worried me. The Thor was still in the research and development stage, but its tests had been getting progressively more successful. If there had to be a failure, I thought, why in this mission? Why the failure? What happened? I thought of the oft-quoted figure of 300,000 tiny parts and realized the odds were long, but, frankly, I had confidence in the Thor. I figured a hitch might develop in the other stages, for they were untried in this combination.

I left the blockhouse and was one of the first to drive off. I headed the car across the Cape to Hangar L where we had our post-mortem meetings. It was a long drive, a weary three miles. The sun was high now and it was just another hot, sunny, summer Sunday morning in Florida. There were flies and bugs, a rabbit jumping here or there in the low undergrowth and a faint veil of smoke from the rocket engine hovering over the area around the pad and riding down toward the sea on the back of a breeze.

The office in which we met is 20 by 30 feet and there was a list posted on the door indicating who was required at the meeting. It was a solemn group. We were fatigued, for none of us had slept for nearly 24 hours. Three windows were covered with black shades and a green chalkboard hung between two of them, and on it were pertinent facts about the short-lived flight. Telemetry data sheets hung on wires strung along the walls.

Each sheet had five wiggly horizontal lines, each representing the time history of some function taking place in flight. For the lunar probe, twelve of these sheets covered the functions of the first- and second-stage telemetry. This was what we were most interested in now.

The room has two large wooden conference tables which are pretty well beat up—and their poor appearance today fitted into the mood and spirit of our meeting. The tables are placed end to end along the 30-foot dimension of the room and arranged in front of the green chalkboard. Office chairs are placed behind the table facing the board, and the rest of the room is furnished with modernistic school-desk chairs. The room can accommodate forty-five to fifty seated, but we had

126

a dozen or so more standing at the meeting in Hangar L that morning.

My job was to co-ordinate the meeting and set up task groups for the Flight Test Working Group which would analyze the problems which we found. Earle Wollam took over for me at the blockhouse and reported later with pad conditions. It was a pretty intense gathering. People started to congregate in the room right after the firing and took quick looks at the data sheets. They stood in small groups around the room examining the sheets, recounting countdown experiences or giving opinions on the cause of the mishap. It would have been an easy matter for a stranger, properly cleared, of course, to walk into the room and tell whether the shoot had been successful. We were tired, unshaven, unhappy, wondering to ourselves, not daring to ask, if we were responsible for the failure.

When the principals appeared I called the meeting to order and reviewed what we knew and called on experts in various fields to interpret data for the whole group. I discussed the countdown, the problems, the holds, the decisions—anything that could give us a clue. I called on Rocketdyne's John Fitzwater, and he gave a report on the first-stage performance, since it was the Rocketdyne engine which lifted the Thor off the pad. The major task group appointed for further study was composed of Fitzwater, Douglas' Jerry Coleman, and Space Technology Laboratories' Mort Goldman.

The meeting lasted an hour. The tired men then left for their homes. By now the whole world knew we had tried—and failed. General Schriever, General Yates, and Mr. Johnson had met with newsmen back at Patrick Air Force Base in the base theater and had answered questions. They gave a disappointing report, but one underlined with hope.

The failure was reported as being located in the first-stage propulsion system, one of those one-in-a-hundred chances. But it caused an explosion and we didn't even have a chance to see the second and third stages in action.

We knew that next time we would still be working with an unknown quantity—but we did have confidence in the new countdown format. It worked: we had fired only four minutes late.

That was something.

# CHAPTER 13

The failure of the first lunar probe attempt sat like a worrisome monkey on our shoulders. And the fact that it happened the way it did, in the explosion of the first-stage Thor, didn't help the spirits of our Douglas team. We wanted very much to see the whole package go.

The lunar probe program announced in March had set up three Air Force probes, and we were ready to move right into the second attempt. The moon would be in position in a lunar month, about twenty-seven days, and we temporarily set that time as a goal. However, when data had been reduced by Douglas, Rocketdyne, and the other West Coast experts, we knew a September firing was out of the question. We knew we could benefit from the knowledge gained in the first shoot, but we needed time to apply it to the next shoot.

Our enthusiasm rose again when we got back to work.

129

We worked at a high pitch, putting in time on both the lunar probe project and the continuing program of testing and developing the Thor weapon. This lunar probe had to go, had to go, we told ourselves. The odds were stacking up against us. Our next shot would be the last throw but one. It was set for 3:42 A.M., October 11, 1958.

The time and date ran continuously through my mind. The new vehicle was 130—and we had a lot of work to do on it. We did not schedule a mock countdown for the second probe. We were confident, perhaps overly confident, that the operations of the first attempt had demonstrated that we could fire at a particular time of day. This was one of the rewarding aspects of the first attempt. In the backs of our minds we also knew that 127 had been exceptionally trouble-free. Would 130 be just as good a missile? To make certain that missile and men were prepared for the second shoot, we would perform a flight-readiness firing, which is a short-duration test run of the first-stage engine.

The flight-readiness firing differs from a mock countdown in that the engine is actually fired for 30 seconds at the completion of the countdown, and 30 seconds of firing on a static test stand can give you a good idea of what is right or wrong.

We started a flight-readiness countdown on September 30 and ran through a simplified countdown procedure. The total countdown was just six hours with no built-in holds because there was no need to fire at a particular time of day. But the test was never completed. One of those unforeseen problems arose at the last minute and we decided to "scrub" the test at T-35 minutes.

At this point we were pretty disheartened about the whole situation. Missile 130 had given us more trouble than Missile 127 from the beginning and checks had not gone smoothly. We licked the problems as we went along, and we thought we were in good shape for the flight-readiness test, but we missed it. Pressure was building up. Here it was September 30 and we had an October 11 target date. We felt our backs were against the wall. There was much speculation in the press about the second attempt, and the public's eyes were fastened on Cape Canaveral. We decided to go ahead. It looked reasonable to try the very next day for the flight-readiness firing, so we detanked the Thor missile—taking out kerosene and liquid oxygen, our fuel and oxidizer respectively—and worked hard to correct the trouble discovered in the countdown.

The next day we tried again. We released the flight-readiness countdown at 8:30 A.M., October 1, and again things were not as clean as we had hoped. But they were adequate for the firing. At times I was ready to chuck the whole thing and wished that, by some miracle, we could be presented with another missile to work with. Was this one going toward the moon?

After several holds and recycles, we proceeded to zero and ignition at 3 in the afternoon, and the firing was successful. Our spirits rose. Maybe, we thought, we've just got a temperamental missile which would perform under pressure. But this made the thing too human—and we knew too many things could go wrong.

Our data critique meeting after the firing showed we had more work to do. In our hands now was a massive amount of information. We decided our engine was airworthy, our missile was airworthy and we could proceed with plans for the October 11 firing date. We swung into action again, this time with the big goal fixed in our minds.

The next step was putting the second and a dummy third stage on Missile 130. The second stage was checked out. The deficiencies discovered in the flight-readiness firing were corrected, repaired and the missile made ready for flight. We had integrated the information received from the first probe's data, and we felt we would not have a repeat of that performance. Confidence was high now, despite the fact that Missile 130 had given us a large-size share of headaches. The big question, even with all these checks, rechecks, and information, was whether the still-untried upper stages would work.

Douglas' Bob Johnson came down for the second shoot, and he set the odds at ten to one, and I think those odds were pretty accurate. A lot of things had to go in series, and one break in the chain, no matter how minute, could ruin the whole thing.

We checked the days off the calendar quickly now. Our checks on T-2 day were conducted on Wednesday, October 8, and our checks on T-1 day on Thursday, October 9. We had our T-1 day meeting on the after-

The mating of the Aerojet-General, second stage to Missile 130.

The gantry being pulled back from Missile 130 prior to the final countdown.

noon of October 9 at five o'clock. There were no severe problems.

Now we were ready for the third and fourth stages. The third stage had not been mated previously because of its live (solid) propellant; the payload fourth stage was ready to be carried from the hangar at last.

Complex 17-A now had the missile, the long, pencil-shaped moon rocket, mated and ready to go.

The second and third stages of a space probe vehicle are assembled.

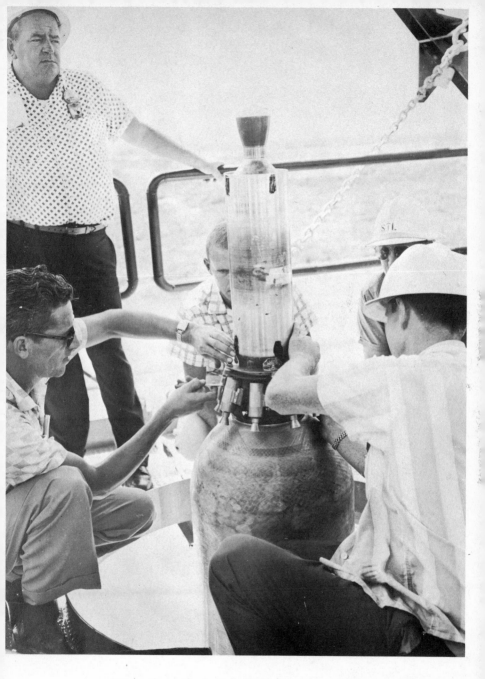

Fitting the payload stage, "Pioneer," to the rocket–propellant
third stage manufactured by the Alleghany Ballistic Laboratory.

# CHAPTER 14

The meeting on October 9 showed that it was possible to go into the countdown the next day. And I was handed a good weather report:

"10/10, 2400 EST, to 10/11, 0900. Cloud cover .2 to .3 cu. bottom 2,000, top 5,000; .4 cirrus. bottom 35,000, top 40,000. Visibility better than ten miles. No precipitation. No thunderstorms. Surface winds, E 5 knots. No upper winds above 45 knots below 80,000 feet. No strong shears. Temp. Max 86, Min 73."

Our firing time was still set for 3:42 A.M., October 11, 1958.

Experience gained in the Able shoots and the first lunar probe countdown showed that we should schedule our second-stage propellant loading task at night rather than in the daytime. This is an extremely hot job for those engaged in it, and the heavy protective clothing causes much perspiration—and boots fill with sweat. So

138

we arranged for the second-stage loading task to start at 4 A.M., the morning of October 10, when it was cool, with personnel reporting to the station at 3:30 A.M. The time between the second-stage loading and the start of the last portion of the countdown was originally planned as two hours. In this countdown we decided to extend this time to enable us to load the second stage at night and in the early morning hours.

Earle Wollam served as Test Conductor in this portion of the countdown. I was at home and I slept until early in the morning of the 10th. I drove to the Cape at 10 A.M., and, by this time, Earle had gone home for some rest. The second stage was loaded and the missile was in a stand-by condition. We were in a no-work period, and the last portion of the countdown was due to start at 4:32 P.M. This was a good plan, but time hung heavy on my hands. I had a lot of things to do, but I would rather have been in the countdown than waiting for the last part of it to begin.

That time, however, came soon enough. At 4:32 P.M., October 10, 1958, the T-time stood at T-490 minutes. Now we were on the road. We were thirty minutes into our engine checks and off and running. In eleven hours we hoped to see lift-off. This was the "beginning" of the second lunar probe countdown. It came two months after the first failure, just months after first planning and after months of sleepless, hard nights of asking ourselves if we could do it—and reassuring ourselves that we could.

Our first move was to release the electrical checks,

139

and we moved ahead until 5 P.M., when we got a report from the range that telemetry ELSSE (Electronic Sky Screen Equipment) was "no-go." Now what? I asked myself. This meant that in the opinion of the ELSSE operators, they could not furnish range-safety information during the flight. We had to have ELSSE telemetry or the Range Safety Officer wouldn't let us fly. ELSSE is a sort of missile tracking system which uses the telemetry transmitter in the missile as a beacon for range-safety purposes. Properly analyzed, it can tell the Range Safety Officer whether the missile is off course. We knew from our signal strength reports that our telemetry signal was adequate, and yet the ELSSE ground station was saying "no-go." We got in touch with the ELSSE operators and also had some consultations of our own in the blockhouse. Apparently we were getting the "no-go" report because the signal strength at the ELSSE site was too low. We decided the reason for the low signal strength was probably that the service tower was attenuating the telemetry signal. Past data confirmed that the signal strength at the ELSSE site always went up when the tower was removed from around the missile. Therefore we reasoned that this would happen again—and crossed our fingers. We decided not to do anything with telemetry or to ELSSE and proceed and hope that we got a "go" report in the terminal countdown.

6:35 P.M. We started fueling the Thor.

7 P.M. Intercom problems. Able facilities loop, over which upper-stage work was accomplished, was not

working properly. We informed the Superintendent of Range Operations of noise on the loop, and he sent wiremen to the blockhouse to work on this during the countdown. Intercom problems cause a lot of concern because every intercom box is used in the countdown. So when a box or the whole communication system goes out it is necessary to juggle the location of people in the blockhouse and to work around the problem. We had to do this while the system was under repair.

7:30 P.M. Fueling proceeded on schedule with no problems, but at the end of fueling we had a quick decision to make. We had two sources of information telling us how much fuel was aboard the Thor. These were the flowmeter (similar to a gas pump) in the fuel-propellant line on the ground and the missile weight system. These two sources gave us different answers for the amount of fuel aboard. Loading is very critical, of course, so in an attempt to find out which figure was correct we started to pull the small cover plate off the top of the fuel tank to find out where the real fuel level was below the top of the tank. While the plate was being taken off, a recalculation of the two numbers that were available showed that both systems did agree and showed the proper amount aboard. The cover was replaced and we proceeded with igniter installations.

9 P.M., T-222 minutes. The destruct test was run.

11:06 P.M. We manned for LOXing, the exercise during which we put liquid oxygen aboard the first-stage Thor.

12:27 A.M., October 11. LOXing and regulator settings started. We found out at this time we had another headache, for the AZUSA ground station was inoperative. AZUSA is a part of an impact prediction system, a system which calculates the predicted point of impact of a missile in flight for range-safety purposes.

1:30 A.M. The tower began to move back slowly, and it was now T-72 minutes. The operation took six minutes.

Now the missile stood in the glare of the searchlights, and up and down the coast thousands could see it sitting there bathed in light. You get a strange sensation when the tower moves. If you are on the deck near it, you swear the tower is standing still and the missile is falling forward. You have to do a double-take to make certain.

2:07 A.M. We reached T-35 minutes at 2:07. It is at this point that we go into a one-hour no-work period. This time we still had work going on, so it was not a complete no-work period.

2:35 A.M. Dick Pugeau, Pad Control, reported to me that he was having trouble putting the small cover plates on the engine section of the missile. These plates were screwed in, and his mechanics were having a hard time aligning the plates and the screw holes. This was a problem we never dreamed would come up. It was such a simple task I couldn't believe what I heard. We planned to release the count at 3:07 A.M., but Dick swore he was having difficulty.

After a while I checked with him on the pad.

"What are you doing out there, Dick? Hurry up."

142

"Ted, we can't get the screws in."

"Come on, Dick, it's a simple job. Hurry."

"Got one in, Ted."

A few minutes later, "Another screw in."

Then, "Four, five. . . ."

I was getting frantic. What a situation! All this trouble just to screw on cover plates. Bill Duval and I started making some rapid calculations on the number of screws we could safely leave out. The situation was ridiculously funny in some ways—now that I look back on it—but we were in no laughing mood. Time was critical.

"Got another one in," Dick reported over the intercom.

"Hurry, Dick. You've got to get inside the blockhouse," I told him. "We start the terminal countdown in ten minutes. Hurry."

Finally, at 3 A.M., just seven minutes before we had to release at T-35, Dick reported that the covers were on and everything was O.K. I shook my head. What a missile 130 had been! We picked up the count at 3:07, T-35 minutes and counting.

Again I had that old reaction, the tenseness, the anxiety, the feeling that we were on the brink of the unknown. We've got to do it, I said to myself, we've just got to do it this time.

# CHAPTER 15

We began, that warm October morning before dawn, the most dramatic countdown in history. As I stood in the blockhouse I realized all over again what a momentous day this was. Here for the second time—unless the Russians had tried—man was ready to attempt to send a rocket toward the moon. Here was man ready to step from the cradle of his own planet. Man had explored the far corners of his earth, reached the bottoms of the oceans, soared to the tops of the clouds, searched for knowledge in the atom, but never had he broken the bounds of his own planet, earth. He was ready to try.

Outside the blockhouse on the launching pad was an 88-foot, four-stage missile, one of the most powerful man has ever built, a missile capable of pushing an instrument-loaded capsule 24,000 miles an hour through the unknown miles of outer space.

"Five seconds, four, three, two, one—*mark*, T-35," I said.

144

Close up of Missile 130 on launching pad during final countdown.

The terminal count had begun.

I opened the intercom key again and said: "Give me your attention on the loop, please, this is the Test Conductor. . . . At zero time there will be no mass exodus to the back of the blockhouse. Personnel will stay in their seats. . . . Personnel will stay in their seats until all operations have been completed, *then*, for nonoperating people, there will be an orderly, I repeat, *orderly* walking to the back of the blockhouse. Pad Safety will open the blockhouse when he gets the clearance. I again emphasize there is to be no disorder after T-zero."

It must have sounded like a pretty harsh message, and I imagine I was a real bastard to some of the guys, but there had been too much noise, too much shouting and yelling after the first shoot. I didn't want a repeat. We remain an operating team after lift-off and I didn't want this work interfered with.

We were in the terminal countdown now. The most anxious moments were here. There is that second or so in which you are kept tied up in knots between the Talker's command, its execution and the affirmative reply. For instance, the Talker says, "Telemetry on," and the console operator answers "On." Then the operator waits to make sure that telemetry has, indeed, come on and is working properly.

The countdown continued. . . .

"T-nine minutes—*mark*."

"Blockhouse vents closed, no smoking."

I put out my cigar. The air-conditioning vents

slammed shut. We were sealed in now. Just nine minutes to go, if all went well.

At T-6 we broke the countdown into 30-second intervals.

"T-five minutes, thirty seconds—*mark*."

"Pressurize ground fuel start tank."

"Roger."

"Report ground fuel start tank pressure."

"Good."

"Relieve cells."

"Cells relieved."

"What is the LOX weight?" I asked.

I was told it was 200 pounds low. This was good, we would be completely tanked up by firing time.

The Superintendent of Range Operations came on the loop.

"You made it, Brandy," he said. "ELSSE is 'go,' both sites."

This was a milepost. I smiled at Griffith. We had gambled on ELSSE signal strength coming up after the tower had moved. It had. We had sweated the thing out and finally got the word only six minutes before lift-off.

"T minus ninety seconds—*mark*."

"Inverter internal."

"Internal."

"Eighty seconds—*mark*."

"LOX tank pressure."

"Good."

"Seventy seconds—*mark*."

"Electronics system internal."

148

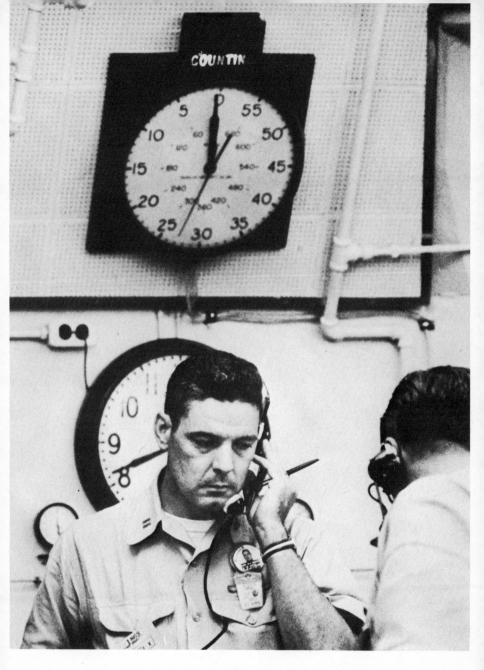

The Field Project Officer waits out the seconds prior to the launching of the "Pioneer".

"Internal."

"Sixty seconds—*mark*."

"Telemetry internal."

"Internal."

"Charts high speed."

"High speed."

"Check all batteries."

"Roger."

"Fifty seconds."

"Close LOX bleed valves."

"Closed."

"Arm."

"Armed."

"Able power to lock-up."

"Roger."

"Forty seconds—*mark*."

"Check inverter."

"Good."

"Able to ready."

"Ready."

"Thirty seconds—*mark*."

"Start tanks."

"Pressurized."

"Open vernier fuel vent."

"Open."

"Check arm."

"Arm."

"Twenty seconds . . . nineteen-eighteen-seventeen-sixteen-fifteen-fourteen-thirteen-twelve-eleven-ten . . ."

Then at ten seconds—trouble. We should have had

an O.K. from Engine Control by now. Where was it?

The Timer reached 10—and Major Myers threw the hold switch. The Timer stopped. We had stopped the countdown just ten seconds before lift-off. We had not received indication from Engine Control that the small tanks had pressurized properly.

"Ten seconds and holding," the Timer said.

We have an intricate set of checks and balances built into every countdown, so if the proper reaction is not obtained from every command, from every switch thrown, we have to hold. Start tanks were pressurized at 30 seconds; we had not received an O.K. from Engine Control at 10 seconds; we called a hold.

Just as we called the hold we got the O.K. from Engine Control. I had to move fast. There was not a half-second to lose. The missile was ready to go.

"On my 'mark,' we will release the count," I cried out. "Three, two, one, we're counting.

"Rearm, please."

The Timer echoed instantly, "Three, two, one, we're counting . . . nine-eight-seven-six-five-four-three-two-one-zero. . . ."

"Ignition!"

At first there was no sound. Then there was a rumble. Then the smoke, the noise louder, the lights on the console clicking off in sequence—the first, the second, the third, the fourth. I stood in my tracks, not moving.

Lift off! Go, go, go, I said to myself. Go! Go! Go!

The lift-off was clean. The missile programmed properly. At 50 seconds we opened the back of the block-

Missile 130 blasts off—first into outer space.

house to nonoperating personnel, and they watched the missile climb into the darkness. The rest of us watched it on telemetry monitors. At 77 seconds we let out a little cheer. We had passed the time of the explosion of the first probe!

I checked telemetry. I could tell the first stage was performing as it should. The Timer read the plus minutes, the Talker read out the remaining items.

"SRO, TC," Brandy Griffith, Test Controller, said to the Superintendent of Range Operations.

"Go ahead, TC."

"You have anything for us?"

"Looking good. . . . All radar has it on track. . . . Still looking good, TC."

"Roger," Brandy said.

We heard the report. Our excitement mounted. Then I could see second-stage telemetry and the second stage was lit. Go, go, go, you're going, go, go.

We could tell now that the second stage was burning about the correct time. The third stage separated, we could tell. I called Duval, who was in his office.

"It looks good," I told him. And he immediately got the West Coast on the wire and reported.

# CHAPTER 16

We knew that Missile 130 had pushed the payload a hell of a long way out. It was on its way. We knew we had done a good job. Where it would go was in the lap of the gods. We left the blockhouse for the post-mortem meeting in Hangar L.

Minutes after lift-off, Air Force public information officers joyfully handed out news releases to the newsmen who had witnessed the launching. The first, which had been previously run off and needed only the time penciled in, read:

CAPE CANAVERAL, Fla.,—The United States launched a three-stage experimental space vehicle at the ATLANTIC MISSILE RANGE at Cape Canaveral, Fla., at 3:42 this morning. The launching was accomplished by the Air Force under the direction of the National Aeronautics and Space Administration and the Department of Defense. It was the second flight test of a number of small unmanned space vehicles designed to gather scientific data as a part of the U. S. International Geophysical Year program which is sponsored by the National Academy of Sciences with the support of the National Science Foundation.

The vehicle is composed of the THOR intermediate range ballistic missile as the first stage—or booster—, a modified VANGUARD second stage, and an advanced version of the VANGUARD third stage. Topping this vehicle is a highly instrumented scientific payload.

A few minutes later, they handed out a second news release:

CAPE CANAVERAL, Fla.,—The second and third stages of the United States three-stage experimental space vehicle launched at the ATLANTIC MISSILE RANGE at Cape Canaveral at 3:42 today have been fired successfully. The launching of the experimental lunar probe vehicle has now been accomplished.

Additional information on the progress of the test will be reported as the data is transmitted to the tracking stations and is, in turn, transmitted to the data reduction center for analysis. This command has no further operational responsibility for this project.

A third release read:

CAPE CANAVERAL, Fla.,—The name "PIONEER" was given today to the payload of the successfully

157

launched U. S. lunar probe rocket, the first man-made object known to escape the earth's gravitational field. After the first 60 minutes of flight into outer space, signals received from the highly instrumented payload indicate that "PIONEER" is proceeding on course at approximately the planned velocity. Interpretation of data received is proceeding on schedule. However, it must be emphasized that there. exist many difficulties and time lags in its analysis.

The Department of Defense transmits the data when received to the National Academy of Sciences' International Geophysical Year Committee for transmission to IGY participants in accordance with IGY procedure.

"PIONEER," launched for NASA by the Air Force, joins other U. S. earth satellites, EXPLORER I and IV, launched by the Army and the Navy-launched VANGUARD.

The payload flew on into space, watched only by electronic eyes. I was ready for the meeting in Hangar L, but already there was something wrong. There was no malfunction, no leaking valve, nothing wrong with the missile. But there was a trifling abnormality which meant that the missile would not make it all the way. This last release, therefore, was a little premature and incorrect, but we were still excited.

The critique meeting was a big contrast to the last one. We had met then after the first lunar probe attempt two months before. Now we had data on the board al-

ready. We knew that the third stage and the eight vernier rockets had fired. We had two conflicting reports,
however: one that the velocity was sufficient and that
it was on its way, and the other that the velocity was
low and it wouldn't make it.

All we knew for sure was that it was going on one
hell of a long trip! There was much excited talk, back-
slapping praise and handshaking. We reviewed the data
and broke up at 5:30 A.M. This was much quicker than
usual, but who wanted to look at problems after a shoot
like that?

General Yates had called a press conference at Patrick, and Bill Duval and I, as well as Larry Vitsky of
Douglas public relations, George Butler, Bob Johnson,
Earle Wollam, and others attended. Louis Dunn and
Bob Bennett, of Space Technology Laboratories, were
up front with General Yates. They were giving reporters
and television men a briefing on what happened and
where we stood. Dr. Dunn said the reason the velocity
was low and that all eight vernier rockets had to be fired
was undoubtedly due to the fact that the first-stage
flight path was high.

We knew that the missile flight path had been slightly
high. We saw this on the radar charts that were available at the post-mortem meeting. It wasn't clear to us
that this high flight path was beyond the specifications
previously established or that it was responsible for
the entire amount of payload velocity error.

This difference of opinion clouded the picture but
slightly. The payload was on its way. It ultimately went

71,300 miles before falling back into the earth's atmosphere and burning up.

*We had done it! We were first in outer space. This flight established a record for the greatest altitude and greatest velocity ever achieved by a man-made object.* The missile also established other great firsts: the high-altitude measurement of radiation and of the earth's magnetic field, and it marked the first use of a vehicle in space as a radio repeater station achieving direct communication from one point on earth through the space vehicle to another point almost halfway around the world.

After General Yates's conference we were interviewed in the auditorium at Patrick by several news people. When I walked out of the darkened building it was bright daylight and I was blinded by it. Then I realized I had been up a solid 24 hours. I drove the Healey toward Cocoa Beach and dropped Vitsky off at the Starlite Motel. He said I was supposed to be on a television program about noon that day! Captain Brandy Griffith, Al Donovan, and Bill Newberry of Space Technology Laboratories and I were to be interviewed and were to give our impressions of the flight. I decided to get home and get some sleep. I rode through the Cape again and out the north gate toward Titusville. Annie had heard of our success. She was full of congratulations when I arrived. I felt like a conquering hero, but a tired and dirty hero.

I filled the tub with water and soaked. Annie had to go out shopping and took the kids. After I got out of the

160

bathtub I stretched out on the sofa for a couple of minutes. At 11 A.M. there was a big meal on the table and I was being gently awakened by Annie. I wanted to share a little of the experience with her, but neither time nor security had ever afforded that pleasure. We listened to news broadcasts during lunch and found, to our surprise, that we were the Wright brothers and Columbus rolled into one.

When I arrived back at the Cape I found the others just as tired as I was, and the elation had somewhat worn off. By this time we knew for certain that Pioneer was not going to go all the way. There was no doubt now.

After the program I returned to Titusville and climbed into bed. Annie woke me in time to go to a party at the Douglas House that evening. The place was filled with Douglas, Rocketdyne and Space Technology Laboratories people, news folks, sober people, drunk people—all kinds and all shapes. And all happy. It was a good party, and we left it and went next door to the Starlite where another party was going on. Rocketdyne was tossing a party of its own. As we walked over we saw someone splashing around the swimming pool. Someone had been thrown in and was diving for his false teeth.

CHAPTER 17

We slept late the next morning. When I finally awoke, my head was throbbing. I walked out to the driveway in my pajamas and picked up the morning newspaper. The headlines told the story of the moon shoot. It was good reading—until I got to the small print.

The papers hailed the great scientific achievement. We were first in outer space, but it was only human for the question to come up: if it went that far out, why didn't it go all the way? The only answer available was the reason Dr. Dunn had given. I agreed in part. The high programming had caused some of the low velocity, but our data indicated that the high programming had been within specifications. The first and second stages, apparently, had performed well. Brigadier General O. J. Ritland, vice-commander of the Air Force Ballistic Missile Division, confirmed the fact that the Thor had performed as scheduled later in the day.

162

The cluster of vernier rockets that was attached to the base of "Pioneer".

As is often the case in subtle disabilities such as this, analysis must await careful review of final data and computer computations. The third stage carried no telemetry and could not tell its own story; its performance had to be inferred from other data sources. We were looking for a clue.

But we still felt pretty rosy. There was no question about it, we felt pretty proud of the vehicle and the test. I read the papers carefully, listened to news reports on radio and watched General Schriever that night on television.

Dr. T. Keith Glennan, administrator of the National Aeronautics and Space Administration, received this wire:

Please convey to all who took part in yesterday's scientific space probe my sincere congratulations on this splendid achievement. This flight has truly pioneered in deep penetration into outer space. Already it is clear that it will yield knowledge of great benefit to mankind in adding to an understanding of the universe in which we live.

It was signed "Dwight D. Eisenhower."

While we had been celebrating the night before, much had been happening at the communication points around the world. The missile's log reads like this:

The 150,000 pounds of thrust lifted the giant missile off the ground at 3:42.5, just five seconds off schedule, and the Thor, gulping tons of fuel a minute, burned its

165

full 160 seconds and pushed the missile 50 miles up. The first stage fell away and the second stage ignited; the second stage burned for 110 seconds. The protective shield which covered the payload was jettisoned. Then the third stage took over and this solid propellant stage burned for its correct duration. The payload, which is the final stage, was wrapped with small vernier rockets —to be used for extra propulsion, if needed—and the retro rocket, which would throw it into orbit around the moon. The payload itself was flying through space.

It was evident to the Space Technology Laboratories' vernier firing crew that the velocity after third-stage burnout was not sufficient and the moon mission would fall short. A decision had to be made. It was apparent that more speed was needed. Now, how many of the payload vernier rockets should be fired? At T-plus-8 minutes all of them were triggered and the payload picked up fifty miles an hour. This was not enough speed increase.

The center of activity shifted to the West Coast. The Inglewood, California, Data Reduction Center took over. Reports came in from stations in the States, from Singapore, from Hawaii and England. The stations were picking up the coded telemetry on radiation levels, micrometeorite activity and magnetic fields. Position data was fed into giant IBM 704 computers so that a flight path could be predicted. The computer said, "Peak altitude, 79,000 miles."

The payload was decelerating in the cold blackness of space, a tiny object in the vast fields of the sky

166

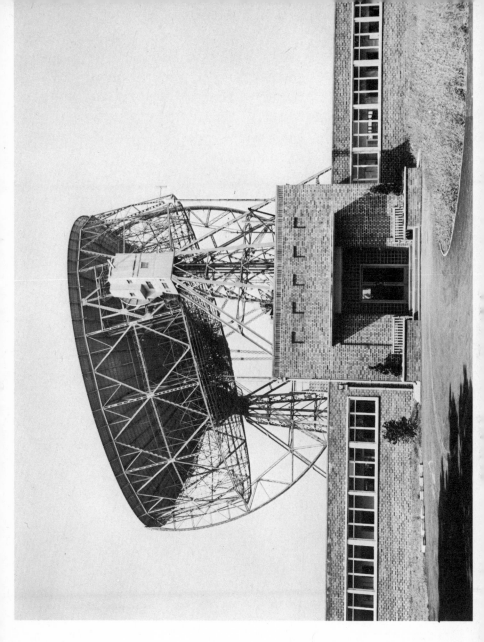

Main control building for the radiotelescope near Manchester, England.

beyond the sight of man but not beyond his electronic hearing. Scientists and astronomers around the world were keen with excitement as they listened to the valuable data coming back from space for the first time.

The following releases were made by the Department of Defense:

### Oct. 11, 1958, 3:45 P.M., EST

The position of the United States lunar probe vehicle Pioneer at 3:45 P.M., EST, was approximately 1.7 degrees North Latitude: 129.8 degrees West Longitude and approximately 65,000 statute miles above the earth's surface.

The Pioneer's velocity was approximately 3,000 miles an hour.

### Oct. 11, 1958, 8:15 P.M., EST

At 7:09 p.m., EST, today the Singapore tracking station commenced tracking the Pioneer lunar probe. With this contact, all ground stations comprising the world-wide network of stations established to monitor the flight of the Pioneer have successfully obtained telemetering information.

The altitude of the Pioneer at 7 P.M., EST, was 67,850 statute miles. Contact with Hawaii is continuing.

### Oct. 11, 1958, 8 P.M., EST

A statement was released by Dr. W. W. Kellogg, Acting Chairman, Satellite Panel, National Academy of Science, IGY Committee:

Scientific data has been received for the past 15 hours from the Pioneer in its history-making flight into outer space. Data has been received at Millstone, Mass., Manchester, Eng., the Air Force Missile Test Center at Cape Canaveral and from Hawaii. The data being received includes radiation data, micrometeorite data, internal temperature, magnetic field measurements, and vehicle spin rate information. The TV camera has not yet been turned on.

The radiation data of most interest was obtained at Manchester and very preliminary examination indicates a maximum reading of approximately four roentgens per hour at approximately 10,000 miles altitude. This value was obtained by quick look examination at Manchester and must be considered as preliminary. Detailed data reduction of the data will be required before specific trends and final values can be established.

Only one micrometeorite hit has been recorded in the first 12 hours of flight. Internal temperatures stabilized rather rapidly after launch at approximately 40 degrees F. and have during the past four hours gradually been dropping to about 35 degrees F. The nature of the instrumentation for magnetic field readings is such that detailed data reduction is required before specific trends and values can be stated for the magnetic field readings. The vehicle spin rate is holding steady at 110 RPMs.

It was clear now that the missile wasn't going much

Kanae, the Hawaiian tracking site for space probes.

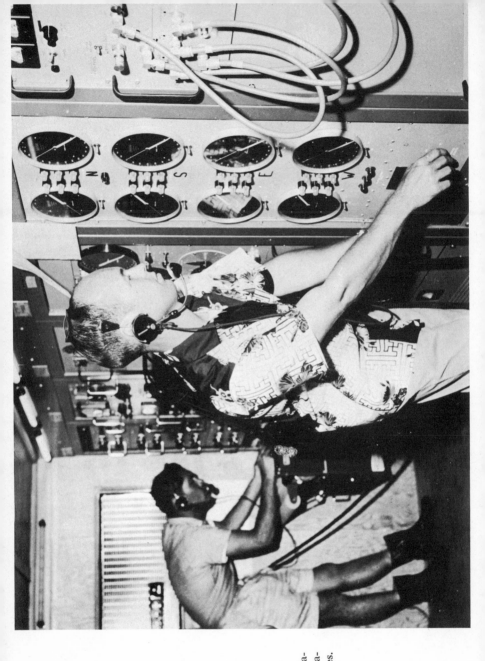

Interior of the Hawaiian tracking station for space probes.

farther than the 67,850 miles already traveled. What to do? It was decided to try to fire the retro rocket, alter the course, and try to throw the payload package into orbit around the earth.

The switch was thrown in Hilo from the mobile trailer parked on the beach. Nothing happened. They tried again, again, again. Still no reaction. Canaveral also tried. No success.

Why hadn't the rocket fired? Data at Inglewood told the story. The temperature inside the payload had dropped from the expected 70 degrees F. to 35 degrees, a level at which the batteries could no longer supply the necessary current to energize the command receiver. Paint and tape had been applied to the exterior of the payload to keep the retro rocket and the instruments from getting too hot or too cold.

The payload was to be exposed to the cold and to the harsh sunlight of space, unfiltered by our atmosphere. It took weeks to perfect the correct pattern of exterior light and dark areas. These were so carefully calculated that the shell was to have been patterned differently for flights on succeeding days.

The low temperature inside the payload indicated a slightly improper payload attitude in space. Here was our clue: the payload was not traveling through space at the correct angle. Since it was mated to the third stage, our theory was that the third stage tipped slightly when it separated from the second stage. This tipping—or change of direction—meant that the energy of the third stage (pushing the payload) was misdirected. This would have produced a low third-stage burnout velocity and improper payload attitude. Combined with the slightly high programming, the velocity error produced was only about 360 miles per hour out of the required 24,000 miles per hour. A small error—but enough in the trajectory to the moon to cause a wide miss.

With the retro rocket silent, missilemen and scientists could do nothing but track the missile on its re-entry path. Somewhere out over New Guinea in the Pacific, the missile reached the end of its journey, burning up in the earth's atmosphere.

The Department of Defense issued the following release at 11:50 P.M., October 12, 1958:

The Hawaiian tracking station lost contact with the U. S. Pioneer lunar probe vehicle at 10:56 P.M. EST. It was the last tracking station in the lunar probe tracking and communications network to receive signals.

Analysis of the data received by the Hawaiian station indicates that the Pioneer re-entered the earth's atmosphere at approximately 11 P.M., EST, and is assumed to have burned up upon re-entry.

The re-entry point was estimated to be over the South Pacific Ocean.

Latitude about 20 degress, South, longitude about 106 degrees West.

No reports of visual observation of re-entry have been received. During the last two hours of the historic flight repeated efforts were made to fire the retro rockets. No confirmation of successful firing was received.

The final velocity was estimated at 34,425 feet per second, the same speed attained shortly after lift-off of the space exploration vehicle at Cape Canaveral at 3:42 A.M. EST, Oct. 11, 1958.

Months later, when the tremendously significant scientific data accumulated by Pioneer was published, the world was to recognize the value of our probe. Through Pioneer, science: (a) determined the radial extent of the radiation band (and first observed that radiation is a band); (b) mapped total ionizing flux; (c) made first observation of hydromagnetic oscillations of the magnetic field of earth; (d) discovered departure of the magnetic field from theoretical prediction; (e) first determined the density of micrometeors in interplanetary space, and (f) made first measurements of the interplanetary magnetic field.

Before the missile took off, someone had scratched this legend on the missile's side: "Katy V. is the most beautiful girl down here, up there, or anywhere else."

Pioneer was the most beautiful missile with the most beautiful disposition man had so far ever seen.

# CHAPTER 18

One day ran headlong into the next between the second
and third lunar probes. A few days after the second shot
we received a wire from California setting the time and
date of the third lunar probe. It said: "NOVEMBER 7,
1:21 AM EST." And in Hangar M, Missile 129 was resting on a rolling framework, a missile ready and standing
in the wings much like an eager understudy in a Broad-
way production.

The days sped past, but they were good days. We
were still basking in the full flush of a great victory, and
our hopes were at high key for the full accomplishment
in our last-scheduled attempt. This was to be our last—
then the Army team from Huntsville, Alabama, would
take over.

Our lives had taken abrupt changes. Cards, letters,
wires poured in from all over the world—nice messages
from complete strangers, relatives, and friends filled

with good cheer and compliments. Our pictures had been in national magazines, my own family was pictured in a French publication, *Fortune* magazine and the *Saturday Evening Post* had articles about us, and many of us had been on coast-to-coast television and radio. Even the man at the filling station seemed to know me and called me by name, others gave me that haven't-I-seen-you-somewhere-before look. All of a sudden a group of security-secluded, unnoticed engineers became minor heroes in the mind of the world—and we were unused to it, didn't know exactly how to take it. Unfortunately, the public tossed bouquets to only a few, when we felt more strongly than before that it was truly a team feat.

Two pieces of mail especially interested me. One was from a woman who was looking for a long-lost relative. His name: Theodore Gordon. It was a different Theodore Gordon. Another letter came from Louisiana State University, my alma mater, and the alumni federation informed me I had been made a life member. I was pleased, flattered, and a little awed by the whole business.

But the last half of the big game still had to be played. The second lunar probe attempt had demonstrated that we had the potential to do the complete job. If things worked as they should, there was no reason to believe that man couldn't break free of this planet, couldn't go anywhere he wanted in the solar system. As far as we were concerned, these facts were now evident, for we had proved many things in our 71,300-mile voyage in the earlier missile.

To say that we had a real burning desire now would be putting it mildly. Now, perhaps, even more than ever before, the vision of our missile flying toward the moon was more vividly etched in our minds. It was more than a theoretical proposition now. I could picture complete success, for I had new confidence in all three working stages and the men who so successfully did the job the last time.

We didn't waste time. While it was nice to receive the plaudits, we had work to do and to do quickly. We had 27 days in which to get the missile ready.

Missile 129 was on the pad quickly—although we didn't rush the mating—and we decided against any special tasks. On the first probe we had run a mock countdown, and on the second we had a flight-readiness firing. We would skip these tests and shoot without them on the third probe.

The biggest headache we encountered as firing time approached was the weather. It rained a great deal of the time, and the winds were high. We didn't know whether nature would stop us or not.

The countdown review meeting (in the ready room of the shop building next to the blockhouse) was held on November 5 at five P.M., and the meeting went smoothly. We elected to start loading the second-stage propellant, as we had done in the second probe, at 4 A.M., on the 6th. This task was completed without complications. Things looked good, and after the task was completed we "impounded" the missile until 2:11 P.M., when the count was again released, this time at T-490 minutes.

178

Missile 129 at night with the gantry in place and tests proceeding.

The gantry being pulled back from Missile 129.

As the evening wore on I grew increasingly worried about the weather. It was nasty. There was much to consider. There are range-safety limitations on the minimum ceiling, which could prevent us from firing; there are practical limitations to the efficiency of people work ing in such rain. They work on a wet, slippery service tower 50 or 60 feet above the ground, buffeted by 50-mile-an-hour gusts. There was still another hindrance, the poor data photographic coverage a low cloud ceiling would produce. We had a Project Command meeting and decided to go ahead. Everyone seemed bent on going ahead, so we agreed. No insurmountable problems presented themselves. The count had been extremely clean and we were keyed up, the foul weather only making the situation more tense than usual.

Now we got another weather report: a cold front was moving up from the south. The prediction was for continued poor weather. We would not let a prediction stop us, we said. By God, if anything stopped us, it had to be the weather itself. The weather would have to be plenty bad. We were ready. The count was going good. The service tower was moved back. The blinking red light on top of the blockhouse appeared brighter in the rain. Searchlights splashed on the Missile 129, the rain hitting the frosted missile spread an even heavier cloud of vapor. It was wrapped in a white blanket.

Someone came up to me in the blockhouse and told me that a message had been chalked on the side of the missile. It was a line from Tennyson. It read, ". . . after it, follow it, follow the gleam."

Now it was T-35 minutes. We had a no-work period. After a 60-minute pause we'd resume the countdown, the terminal countdown. It was 11:46 P.M., November 6, 1958. I walked to the back of the blockhouse to get a breath of fresh air. In the skies I could see a star or two, despite the light patter of rain. I walked back to the Project Command table, propped my feet up high and took out a cigar.

Back on the pad everyone was getting set to come into the blockhouse. They were ready to fasten the last plates on the missile engine section. One man was left inside the missile and he began to ease himself out. As he crawled out, he heard something. He listened again. Then he called me on the intercom. It was an abnormal condition—security prevents me from spelling it out— in the engine section, something we had never run across before.

I called him to the blockhouse immediately, and the Project Command convened in the back room of the blockhouse with our power-plant people. Here we were, just an hour and thirty-five minutes from launch time, and we had a problem totally unknown to us. We heard the description of the noise. My heart sank.

We thrashed out the problem and decided the condition couldn't be readily explained. We had never come across it before, and we didn't have time to run special qualification tests. We could imagine situations that could produce this abnormality and could cause danger in flight. We decided to scrub the test. The scrub was called at 12:35 A.M. on November 7.

182

This was a sad moment. It was the first of our lunar attempts we had to scrub. It was not because of a known missile deficiency or a known missile problem, but because of an unknown, and this colored our despair with apprehension. It was a hard decision, but a wise one.

We started to detank the Thor immediately. It was a terrific letdown, I know, for the others on the project, especially when we didn't know whether we could start the countdown the next day or the next month. We held an emergency meeting in the ready room of the shop building and discussed the earliest possible time we could get back into the countdown. Before getting back, however, we had to identify the source of the trouble.

First, we listed on the board those things which we had to do to requalify the missile before we could get back into the countdown. It seemed reasonable for us to attempt to try again the following day—if and when we found the source of the noise. We outlined the work to be done, the time allotted to each item of work and the people who would accomplish this work. We wanted to be sure our people, already dead tired, did not work around the clock.

We elected to leave propellants in the second stage and start our countdown the next day at T-490 minutes. To make the 2:29 A.M. firing time on the 8th, we had to start at 3:19 P.M. We agreed to go home and try to get a few hours sleep and report in the morning. That gave us from shortly after 2:30 A.M. to 11 A.M., when we'd review the work that was done during the night. We

183

had a new crew to solve the problem and get the missile ready for the countdown.

I headed for Titusville and sneaked into the house as quietly as I could. Annie woke up when I got to the bedroom. "How'd it go, Teddy?" she asked. "Not so good," I told her. "Go back to sleep." I was dead tired and it was 3:15 A.M. I slept fitfully until 8 A.M.

At 10 the next morning I left for the Cape and we went into our 11 A.M. meeting. We found, to our delight, that the unknown was now known and we would be ready to start the count again.

At 3:19 P.M. we resumed the countdown. The count went well. It was exceptionally clean—cleaner, in fact, than on the other lunar probes. We felt good again. The weather was fine, we were going to do it this time, I felt.

As an example of how well the whole thing went, at T-135 minutes we were scheduled to have a two-hour no-work period. We got to this point two hours early, giving us a long four hours in which we had nothing to do.

We resumed the count after our no-work period at 11 P.M. that night—this was still the 7th, a very long day. We LOXed the missile, rolled back the tower and went into the T-35 minute hold at 12:54 A.M., the 8th. At 1:54 we were ready to start the terminal countdown on our last attempt—in this series anyway—to the moon.

The countdown, as I have said, had been wonderfully clean. But, unfortunately, the terminal count was a rough one. The first thing we do in the terminal count is to get the Base pump house to raise its water pressure.

184

Missile 129 blasts off.

We need 175 pounds per square inch to get the desired flow through the deflector plate on the launching pad. The most we could get at the blockhouse was 80 pounds per square inch. This was a problem. We pump thousands of gallons of water through the engine flame deflector plate as the missile lifts off. The intense heat of the missile's flame will crack the steel plate unless it is cooled, and we cool it by pumping 18,000 gallons of water per minute through the holes of the plate. We needed pressure for the job, but it seemed it wasn't available.

We had checked the pressure the day before, but today the pressure was low. I asked Dick Pugeau, Pad Control, to take a car to the pad, which had been cleared, to see if the valves were in the right position or if we had developed a major leak. We continued the count and he was back in five minutes and reported everything was all right. It must have been a pump-house malfunction. We decided we'd take a chance on the deflector plate and go ahead anyway. If the low water pressure caused us to lose a deflector plate, that was a chance of the game. It could be replaced after the firing, and we could not see how the missile could suffer any damage.

Next we had a complication in the destruct system and that had to be resolved. Finally, with only 100 seconds left, the Superintendent of Range Operations in Central Control told us the range was foul. That meant there was some ship or aircraft in the area and he would not clear us to launch. Of all times! I thought.

187

Now what? Our count stopped at 90 seconds. Hoping the range would clear up quickly, I recycled functionally, that is, had the Talker read certain items back but kept the time at 90 seconds. We held at this point for two agonizing minutes. Then the SRO called in. We were clear to proceed. We picked up at 90 seconds and the countdown continued. . . . 60 seconds . . . 40 seconds . . . 20 seconds . . . 19-18-17-16-15-14-13-12-11-10-9-8-7-6-5-4-3-2-1-zero. . . .

All thumbs were up and Eaton looked at me. Then he pushed the button.

"Ignition."

From what we heard in the blockhouse, the third lunar probe was up and off. It went right down the wire. It was programming perfectly. The second-stage performance looked great. At 2:31 we thought we were in business for good. We could see the third-stage separation on the blockhouse telemetry consoles. We left the blockhouse in great spirits. We thought we had another good one.

Duval was somewhat worried. He had watched the launch from the roof of Central Control. He thought the first stage had shut down prematurely because the missile climbed into a bank of clouds and he swore it looked like a shutdown. I quickly told him this was not true.

We still thought all had gone well when we got back to the hangar for the critique meeting. We then had reports that the third stage had not ignited.

We were reluctant to accept the information. It just

188

didn't seem true. Not the solid propellant third stage. Certainly the report was wrong. We were so keyed up we just didn't want to believe it.

We called Hal Thomas in California and gave him the disappointing word in such a way as not to violate security. Hal had taken over Bromberg's job as project engineer for Thor. It wasn't a nice beginning for a man who had been on the job such a short time.

At the critique meeting we reviewed the first- and second-stage performance. What a disappointment! Missile flight had been perfect to that point. We had a perfect two-stage flight, everything right and normal. It was just where it should have been and at the right velocity.

Why didn't it go? Just some two-bit part. That's no exaggeration. The third stage is a solid propellant. All that had to happen was ignition. It was really insignificant. With that failure went our dreams.

The National Aeronautics and Space Administration wrote a finish to the story with this news release from Washington:

The following information about the space probe was released this morning by NASA, based on analysis of tracking information at the end of second-stage burning by the Data Reduction Center of Space Technology Laboratories, Inc.:

Preliminary calculations of the trajectory of the space probe indicates that it reached an altitude of about 1,000 miles before re-entering the atmosphere over East Central Africa, and disintegrating due to air friction. This was approximately 7,500 miles from Cape Canaveral. Maximum velocity was estimated at 16,000 miles per hour.

We learn, or we think we learn; we incorporate all we learn and try again, and yet there are always imponderables, unpredictables. The accomplishment of our dream had to be left to others. There was no question now; it could be done.

But on this day, being a frustrated man, I was swamped with depression. I went home as soon as I could.

"I'm sorry, Teddy," Annie said.

✽   ✽   ✽   ✽

*On January 2, 1959, the Soviet Union launched a cosmic rocket named Mechta. The spherical 797-pound payload passed the moon and went into orbit around the sun, a true artificial asteroid. Now at a distance of roughly 100 million miles it quietly circles the sun once every 450 days. It will probably continue to do so for all eternity.*

*At 12:10:54 A.M., EST, on March 3, 1959, six and a half months after the first Air Force lunar shot, the Army, in their second attempt and using a countdown format similar to the revolutionary Thor lunar probe countdowns, placed an instrumented payload in the vicinity of the moon. Since their flight plan called for speeds in excess of escape velocity, the payload, Pioneer IV, went past the moon and into orbit around the sun.*

190

*It now circles the sun every 395 days at an average speed of about 65,000 miles per hour. Its aphelion is 106.1 million miles and its perihelion is 91.7 million miles. It, too, may circle the sun forever.*

*Pioneer IV passed within 37,000 miles of the moon, leading it and below. The probe was tracked for 82 hours after launch when its batteries were depleted. The maximum velocity achieved was 24,789 miles per hour, 196 miles per hour below the desired velocity, but sufficient to send America's first payload into the cosmos. The payload itself was conical in shape and weighed 13.4 pounds. It was launched from NASA's Juno II vehicle; an Army Jupiter IRBM with four solid propellant upper stages.*

So, October 11, 1958, the day of our second lunar probe shot, forever marks man's entry into outer space. This, I am proud to say, was done from that sand trap called Cape Canaveral. I guess I'll always have an affection for the place.

193